AN ILLUSTRATED HISTORY OF

STEAMSHIPS

AN ILLUSTRATED HISTORY OF
STEAM

A.F.L. DEESON

SPURBOOKS LIMITED

[c1976]

SHIPS

Published by Spurbooks Limited
6 Parade Court, Bourne End,
Buckinghamshire

© A.F.L. DEESON 1976

ISBN 0 904978 05 2

Designed and Produced by
Mechanick Exercises, London

Typesetting by
Inforum Limited, Portsmouth
Printed and bound in Great Britain
by Redwood Burn Limited
Trowbridge and Esher

CONTENTS

ILLUSTRATIONS

1
THE
PIONEERS

The story of the development of the steamship really begins in the early 18th century when the concept of steam power caught the imagination of many inventive men, in Britain, on the Continent and in America.

Their aspirations were founded on finding a steam method of propelling paddle-wheels, which themselves were known 2000 years ago as a method of propulsion. Medieval manuscripts preserved in the *Bibliothèque Nationale* in Paris indicate that the invasion of Sicily under Claudius Caudex, before the birth of Christ, was accomplished with the help of boats which had paddle-wheels turned by oxen and there is certainly a bas-relief of the early 6th century AD which shows what is believed to be a Roman war vessel fitted with six small paddle-wheels and driven by three pairs of oxen.

Almost inevitably the Chinese and Leonardo da Vinci make their contribution to the paddle-wheel story — the Chinese about the 7th century and da Vinci later, of course, when he produced various mechanical schemes for paddle-wheel propulsion, one of them remarkably similar to the 'pedallo' of today which challenges the holidaymakers' leg muscles around the coasts of most of our seaside resorts. Roughly contemporary with da Vinci's scheme there is also a Chinese wood cut which shows a warship with two pairs of paddle-wheels, armoured with cowhide.

Until comparatively recently it was thought that a Spaniard, Blasco de Gray had proposed a steam-driven boat as early as the 16th century but de Gray's claim to fame has now been discredited: his vessel in fact had paddle-wheels turned by 25 men and the misunderstanding, made by a writer nearly 300 years later, arose from the fact that clouds of steam were said to have arisen from the vessel. However these in fact came from a cauldron of hot water on deck, for use as an offensive weapon.

Salomon de Caus (1576-1635), a native of Normandy in the service of Louis XIII, was perhaps the first man to understand the tremendous power of steam which he utilised in a steam-driven fountain. In one of his works he mentions that it is a force that could move vehicles on land and ships at sea and raise loads but he seems to have taken the matter no further. He had in fact little opportunity to do so because his ideas generally met with the disapproval of Cardinal Richelieu and he was imprisoned in a mad house. Or so one story has it, but other historians deny this and say that de Caus died full of years and honour and point to the fact that a street in Paris is named after him.

David Ramsey, an Englishman and a Groom of the Privy Chamber, may also have had ideas about using steam for the propulsion of boats. In 1630 he obtained a patent for *'diverse new waies and invencons by him found out and perfected, to raise water from lowe pitts by fire, and to make boats, shippes and barges to goe against stronge winde and tyde'.* But if Ramsey had indeed steam in mind nothing came of his ideas.

Undoubtedly the first definite proposal for a steam boat came from Denis Papin who was born in 1647 and died in 1714. He was a French doctor of medicine but, as a Protestant, he fled from persecution to London, and vigorously advocated the propulsion of boats by steam power. He described a steam cylinder fitted with a piston which descended under atmospheric pressure when the steam below it was condensed and proposed that the movement of the piston could be used to revolve paddle-wheels fitted in a boat. Three or four pistons were to be used, each fitted with a separate rack to drive a pinion (with a ratchet mechanism to accommodate the return stroke) on the paddle-wheel shaft, so that a rotary motion could be accomplished.

His concept showed a good practical grasp of the demands of the situation but was never translated into an actual vessel; thus perhaps one cannot give him the title of 'Father of the steamship' although he can take full credit as the inventor of the pressure cooker which he devised as early as 1681!

The principle of reaction had been patented by Thomas Toogood and James Hayes in 1661. They proposed *'a particular way of forceing water through the bottome or sides of shipps belowe the surface or tope of the water, which may bee of singuler use and ease in navigacon'.* The idea was revived by Dr John Allen in 1729 who in that year obtained a patent for a ship which was to be driven by two 'atmospheric' steam engines, as invented by Thomas Newcomen and which were to pump out water at intervals of five seconds and so drive a warship of 1500 tons at a speed of three knots. Newcomen, a Devon blacksmith, who invented the first practical working steam engine, was to inspire all steamboat engineers for the best part of a century, although he had originally designed it to pump out water from mineworkings and it was not easily adapted to marine propulsion.

Jonathan Hulls (1699-1758) certainly based his steam paddle boat on the Newcomen engine. He became involved in the problem which perplexed the captains of Britain's growing Royal and Merchant Navies of the time — that of moving ships in and out of harbour when the wind was non-existent or blowing from an unfavourable direction. Hulls' invention was designed as a 'parking' device and was to have a paddle-wheel at the stern, driven by a Newcomen engine with a vertical single-acting steam cylinder of 30in diameter. On its downward or working stroke this was to lift a weight equivalent to one half of the effective pull. The descent of this weight on the return stroke was to produce the effect of a double-acting engine. To obtain continuous rotation of the paddle-wheel Hulls proposed the use of ratchet wheels, driven by ropes from the piston and from the weight.

In 1736 he obtained the support of a Mr Freeman of Batsford Park near Chipping Camden, who gave him about £160 to develop his invention. He made very detailed drawings and sent them to the Eagle Foundry at Birmingham and selected the River Avon at Evesham for the site of his experiment. A boat was built, probably in Evesham itself, and the trial was carried out some time during 1737. No details have come down to us except that the experiment was a failure, probably due to the fact that he made no attempt to adapt the Newcomen engine and its inherent low power/high weight ratio would have rendered it unsuitable for sustained motion. His financial backing was withdrawn and Hulls, disheartened, gave up the project, dying in poverty in London a few years later. Today Hulls is almost forgotten except by the marine historian but a belated tribute to him as an important pioneer of steam navigation was paid by Cunard when they put up his portrait in one of the state rooms of the *Queen Mary*.

By now, however, 'steam was in the wind', as a marine historian, who should have known better, has said. In 1753, for example, Daniel Bernoulli proposed, admittedly without very much conviction, the steam-powered paddle-ship, and two years later Canon Joseph Gautier published his steamboat proposals in more detail. His vessel was to exert a force of 260 oarsmen and he calculated that the food they would require would exceed in volume the coal required for a Newcomen engine to do the same work. Gautier specified a steam cylinder 33in diameter (thickness included) which seems to indicate 31in effective diameter. This was to have a stroke of 6ft and the piston was to make 15 impulses per minute. He calculated that the total pressure on the piston would amount to 11,000lb and the vertical movement was to be transmitted by chain to a ratchet-wheel mounted on the shaft, which carried rotary oars at its ends. These oars would be turned to propel the boat forward but the ratchet-wheel would leave them idle on the return stroke. He proposed that the steam power could be used also to work the pumps in the boat, to heave anchor and to heat the ovens.

As the second half of the 18th century dawned a number of others made their proposals for steamships, including Pastor J A Genevois, a Swiss; William Henry; and the famous James Watt. It is possible that William Henry, an American, actually put a steamboat on the water but the record is uncertain and if he did it foundered before it could be tried.

If Hulls' and Henry's ventures are thought to be uncertain the credit for putting the first vessel on the water must go to two French artillery officers, Le Comte Joseph d'Auxiron and his partner Le Chevalier Charles Monnin de Eollenai who, encouraged by the French Government, received a formal promise of 15 years' exclusive operating rights if they could drive a vessel by steam. A company was formed and work began on a steam engine and boat on the Ile de Cygnes, an island in the Seine near Paris. The ship was fitted with a twin-cylinder Newcomen steam engine and was taken to Meudon. But on 8 September 1774, before the trials, the counterweight of the beam fell through the bottom of the hull and the vessel foundered. The reason for the sinking was never satisfactorily explained, although some said it was in fact an early form of industrial sabotage by some of the Paris watermen who feared that their livelihood might be in peril if the steamship was successful. This theory has been hawked around generously but it is more likely it was due to the weight of the atmospheric engine and boiler, on the boat's fragile hull.

At this time France was very much taking the lead in steamboats and two years afterwards Jacques Perier constructed a small steamboat fitted with an engine of the equivalent of one horsepower. This received its trials but was found insufficient to drive the vessel upstream against the current and Perier lost interest. However the experiment inspired a French aristocrat, Le Marquis Claude de Jouffroy, to whom the credit must go for inventing the first practical steamship. He was only 24 when he arranged for a vessel to be built at Baume-les-Dames on the River Doubs near Besançon. His first boat, which was tried out in June 1778, was not a success. It was 43ft long with a breadth of 6.4ft and a displacement of about nine tons, fitted with two inclined steam cylinders on the Newcomen 'atmospheric' principle, 22.4in diameter by 64in stroke. The cylinders were made of copper and stiffened on the outside with iron hoops. Chains from the pistons were made to reciprocate two paddles or flaps, one on either side of the boat, 3.2ft wide and 1.6ft deep, which moved in an 8.5ft radius. In principle this raised some interesting new ideas, but the propulsive mechanism proved inefficient.

Undeterred, Jouffroy began work on a second boat. This time he dispensed with the hinged flap mechanism and reverted to paddle-wheels. He avoided some of the earlier mistakes by installing the engine in a long and comparatively narrow boat which was large enough to support a more powerful engine. This time the engine was placed in a horizontal position and the single cylinder was enclosed within the boiler brickwork. The engine was reported to be double-acting which indicates that Jouffroy must have been familiar with some of the improvements to the steam engine that had only been recently introduced by James Watt. The date of 15 July 1783 is an auspicious occasion in the history of the steamship. Jouffroy's *Pyroscaphe* steamed upstream for 15 minutes on the River Saône — the first time in history that a boat had moved against a current by the power of steam.

Jouffroy lost no time in seeking financial backing from the government and submitted a paper to them accompanied by a 1:24 scale model of the steamboat, which can still be seen in the Musee de la Marine in Paris. Ironically, Perier who had already failed to construct a successful steamboat, was called in and his report was that the experiments at Lyons were not decisive. Thus Jouffroy did not get his capital and abandoned work on the project. As a consequence France lost the never-to-be-repeated opportunity of leading in the development of the steamboat. Six years later the Revolution broke out and Jouffroy, as an aristocrat, was forced into premature retirement. He made a partial comeback in the early years of the 19th century when he published a book on the subject and took out a patent. Then 65, he formed a company which built a vessel called *Charles-Philippe,* with paddles operated by a ratchet mechanism which proved effective. The venture was not profitable and Jouffroy retired from view again to surface on one last occasion, when he is recorded as dying of cholera in the Hôpital des Invalides in 1832.

J. Fitch's steamboat
(1785) with
paddle chain

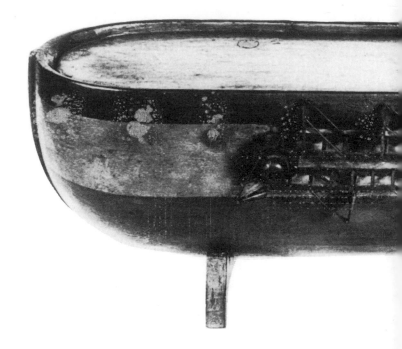

Watt's 'improved' steam engine did much to make
the use of steam for the propulsion of a vessel practi-
cable. And just as Newcomen's steam engine was
wasteful in its driving force, so are paddles which are
of considerable weight and require a great deal of
force to overcome the water's resistance. The first
problem was to make the source of power more effective but at the same time early inventors were working
on early versions of the screw propeller. A Londoner,
Joseph Bramah, was not the first to think of screw propulsion but he worked his ideas out in considerable
detail. In the patent which he took out in 1785 he states
*Instead of the wheel, maybe introduced a wheel with
inclined fans or wings, similar to the fly of a smoke-*

jack, or the vertical sails of a windmill. This wheel or fly maybe fixed on the spindle and maybe wholly under water, when it would be being turned round either way causing the ship to be forced backwards or forwards, as the inclination of the fans or wings will act as oars with equal force both ways, and their power will be in proportion to the size and velocity of the wheel'

To France must go the credit for the first viable steamship, but America was not far behind. In 1785 John Fitch of Windsor, Connecticut, made a steamboat model for the American Philosophical Society at Philadelphia and a year later his first steam-driven boat was tried out on the River Delaware. It performed successfully at a speed of about three miles per hour.

It was in fact a sharp-ended keel boat with a round bilge, curved raked stem and a well-raked sternpost from which the rudder was suspended and worked by a tiller. The paddles, each 12ft in diameter, were placed vertically, six on either side of the boat and were reciprocated by a low-pressure condensing steam engine with one horizontal double-acting cylinder 12in diameter by 3ft stroke.

Two years later, in 1788, Fitch completed another boat 60ft long, which was driven in a similar manner by an engine with one cylinder, 12in diameter. On 12 October 1788, 30 passengers were taken from Philadelphia to Burlington, a distance of about 20 miles in three hours 10 minutes. Fitch's boats were noted for their reliability and he soon initiated a public service on the Delaware with a steamboat propelled by paddles at the stern. This was driven by a beam engine, with one 18in diameter cylinder. Although enthusiastically advertised in the best American fashion the service was not commercially successful and was withdrawn.

Just before the end of the century he turned his attention to screw propulsion and he experimented on a lake near New York with a small boat 18ft long and with a 6ft beam. This was driven by a beam engine with two cylinders. The boiler was an iron vessel with a lid of thick planks, fastened on by an iron bar placed transversely. The cylinders were of wood, barrel shaped on the outside and reinforced with iron hoops. The connecting rod drove a crank on the forward end of the propeller shaft. Unfortunately Fitch died, in 1798, before he could get very far with this latest development.

Meanwhile another American, James Rumsey, was pushing forward with the principle of reaction and in 1787 built and tried the first water-jet steamboat. For

18

this he placed a contract with his brother-in-law, Joseph Barnes, for a wooden hull which, on completion, was floated down the River Potomac from Bath to Shepherdstown where the boiler and engine were assembled. Rumsey dispensed with all external attachments such as paddles or screws and he was in fact the original exponent of hydraulic propulsion for steamboats.

His propelling apparatus consisted of two cylinders placed one about the other with two pistons connected by a common rod. The lower cylinder acted as a pump and was in turn connected to a series of valves fitted in the bottom of the boat. Steam from the boiler was emitted beneath the piston and the upper cylinder and forced the piston to move up and at the same time cause the pump piston to rise and draw in water from the river. When the steam in the upper cylinder was discharged to the condenser atmospheric pressure on the top of the piston forced it down, together with the pump piston below. The water in the lower cylinder was pumped out through a trunk at the stern of the boat and the reaction of this pulsating stream of water propelled the boat forward. On 3 December 1787 his vessel moved against the current of the Potomac with two tons on board, exclusive of the machinery, at the rate of three miles per hour. At the second trial a few days later the boat moved against the current at the rate of four miles per hour. Speed measured in knots was still awaiting adoption for steamships.

Rumsey later came to London in 1788 and built an experimental vessel of 101 tons called *Columbian Maid* at Dover. This was fitted with a water trunk 6in square and a pump 24in diameter which made 22 strokes a minute. On 15 December 1792 it went 'forward against the tide' at Greenwich but before further trials could be arranged Rumsey had a stroke and died in London on 21 December. However the boat was successfully tried on the Thames in February 1793 and

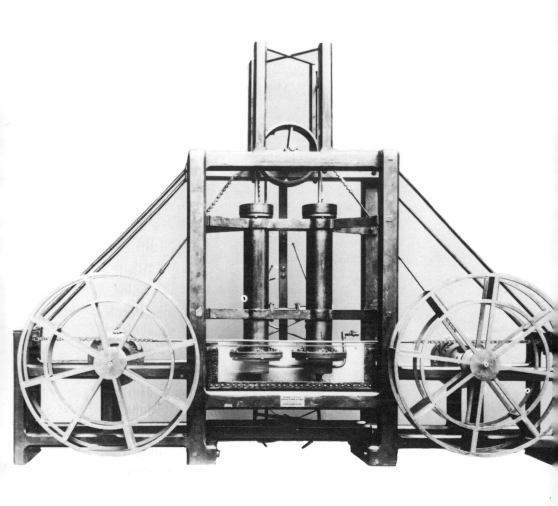

Symington's marine engine (1788)

sailed 'against wind and tide . . . three miles an hour'. Hydraulic propulsion for steamboats has been tried many times since Rumsey's day and of all methods of propulsion it offers the least vibration, but it is also grossly inefficient and wasteful.

Perhaps Rumsey's major contribution to steamboat development was his invention of the pipe boiler. The first boiler he used was a simple iron pot with a lid fastened by rivets and solder but fearing this would be too heavy his pipe boiler was a model of compactness, standing only $3\frac{1}{2}$ft high and yet had a heating surface of 62sq ft. Inside the boiler was a single coiled iron pipe of 2in diameter through which the water circulated.

In the saga of the steamship William Symington should perhaps have rather more credit than he has hitherto received because he was the first person to design an engine specifically for steamboats and he claimed that his invention 'did at least one fifth more work than Mr Watt's, upon the same consumption of fuel'. His engine is still preserved in the Science Museum in London and has two vertical open-topped Newcomen cylinders, 4in diameter by about 18in stroke, in each of which works a piston connected by two chains with a drum which turn in opposite directions alternately. There are two horizontal paddle shafts, on each of which are two loose pulleys with ratchet teeth round their inner flanges. Between each pair of pulleys is a disc keyed to the shaft and fitted with two pawls. Chains from the drum turn these loose pulleys in opposite directions and the teeth on the ratchet wheels are alternately meshed with the pawls and so drove the paddle-wheel continuously in one direction.

This engine was placed in a double-hulled boat and linked with a boiler. The engine was connected by chain gearing with two paddle-wheels situated, one in front of the other, in the space between the two hulls.

Symington's
pleasure boat
c. 1788

On 14 October 1788 the vessel steamed on Dalswinton Lake in Dumfries at the rate of five miles an hour. Those on board included Robert Burns the poet.

Thus encouraged, Symington built a larger engine; the cylinders this time were 18in diameter and were made by the Carron Iron Company. The second vessel went for its trials in November and December 1789 and achieved a speed of about seven miles an hour. Through a mutual friend Symington approached James Watt for his assistance and was shocked to receive a reply which indicated that the inventor considered Symington's engine an infringement of his patent. Indeed, Watt's company, Boulton, Watt & Co indicated that if Symington persisted they would begin legal proceedings. However, Watt's patent expired in 1800 and in the following year Symington

himself patented a paddle-wheel drive arrangement which he fitted in a steam tugboat, the *Charlotte Dundas*. The vessel was built of wood and was financed by Lord Dundas of Kerse and named after his daughter. Lord Dundas was a director of the Forth-Clyde Canal Company and the *Charlotte Dundas* was put into service to draw barges along the canal. She is said to have been a sturdy craft, 56ft long with a beam of 18ft. The engine was of 10 nominal horsepower, placed on the portside of the deck and balanced by the boiler arranged on the starboard side. The engine comprised a single horizontal double-acting cylinder of 22in diameter. A separate condenser was fitted and the air pump was operated from a bell crank driven from the crosshead. Symington's distinctively personal contribution was the method of transmitting power to the paddle-wheel. The piston rod was guided in slides and the connecting rod was linked to a crank which was attached directly to the paddle-wheel shaft.

Trials of the *Charlotte Dundas* were carried out in March 1802 and the performance of the vessel was very successful. The little boat towed two barges to Port Dundas over a distance of 19½ miles in six hours against a strong head wind. Unfortunately the directors of the Forth-Clyde Canal Company became alarmed at the damage subsequently caused to the canal banks by the wash from the paddle of the *Charlotte Dundas* and it was withdrawn from service. Meanwhile Symington had been introduced to the Duke of Bridgwater who was greatly impressed by the *Charlotte Dundas* and ordered eight similar vessels. This was the opportunity that Symington had been seeking for so long but unfortunately the Duke died suddenly in March 1803 and the order was cancelled.

Like many of the steamboat pioneers Symington died a disappointed man.

About the time that Symington was experimenting on Dalswinton Lake two Yorkshiremen, Robert Fourness and James Ashworth, had constructed a small steam-driven paddle-boat which was tried on the river between Hull and Beverley. The result was moderately successful and they constructed another steamboat which was sent to London for assembly.

It had three steam cylinders, which acted on a three-throw crankshaft. Steam was supplied from a copper boiler. The two paddle-wheels on either side were each fitted with 20 fixed radial floats that could be raised or lowered as required. The vessel was satisfactorily tried on the Thames and made several 'voyages' on behalf of the Prince Regent who purchased it later to use as a pleasure boat. Soon afterwards, however, the vessel was burned out in somewhat mysterious circumstances and it was supposed at the time that it had been set on fire by watermen who like the Frenchmen previously, feared the effect of steam power on their jobs.

In the last decade of the 18th century the ideas came thick and fast — although mostly from America, rather than Britain or Europe. Nathan Read, Samuel Morey, William Longstreet, Elijah Ormsbee, Robert R Livingston, Edward West, Nicholas J Roosevelt — all have their small place in the history of steamship development of that time.

Most of them added little or nothing to the rapidly growing fund of knowledge but they were genuine innovators, each 'doing his own thing' and without any idea that perhaps 50 or 100 miles away another man, inspired by the potential of steam, was working virtually on the same lines.

Some, however, made their small contribution: Nathan Read, for example, never seemed to obtain practical or even experimental success with his ideas but he did invent the multi-tubular water-tube boiler. In 1803 Samuel Morey, who had previously built one or two quite successful steamships, obtained his patent for steam engines with crank motion and 12 years later he patented another machine, in which the two steam cylinders revolved about fixed crank-pins. Later he also invented a 'triple pipe boiler' which was used reasonably successfully in a tow-boat. On further trial, however, the steam pressure was found to be very variable at each stroke of the pistons and Morey was unable to cope with the problem. He is also credited with a small-scale experimental engine which may have been a precursor of the 'vapour' or turpentine engine which he himself later patented in April 1826. A 19ft boat in which he placed his vapour engine attained a speed of between seven and eight miles per hour on trial at New York.

In 1798 Nicholas Roosevelt obtained an American patent for a two-cylinder steam engine with cranks set at right angles. His experimental steamboat, the *Polacca* was launched on the River Passaic in the same year but was not a great success, only attaining a speed of about three miles per hour in still water. However Roosevelt continued with his experiments and in 1811 he built the *New Orleans*, the first steamboat to run on the River Mississippi.

In this last decade of the 18th century there were a few British contributions, but they were small. In 1792 Charles, third Earl of Stanhope, obtained patents and conducted experiments in Greenwich Dock with a 'ambinavigator', fitted with vibrators, which were driven by a small steam cylinder 6in diameter and 6in stroke. This engine was put into a flat-bottomed copper-sheathed vessel of 200 tons, without mast or sails, called the *Kent* and was built by Marmaduke Stalkartt of Rotherhithe, an author on naval architecture, and launched in May 1793. The paddles were made to open and shut like the feet of a duck and were constructed of hardwood and reinforced with iron plates; they were placed under the quarters of the vessel and were operated by two steam cylinders of cast iron, developing about 12hp. Steam was supplied from the boiler fed with small coal and dust but no condenser was used because James Watt had refused permission for Lord Stanhope to use parts of his patented design. The tests were undistinguished and the vessel reached only about three miles an hour, but later the engine from the *Kent* is said to have been used by the British Admiralty to drive the first ever steam dredger.

John Smith was another British pioneer of the period, a mechanic from St Helens, Lancashire, who found himself a patron in the shape of a local businessman, Thomas Baldwin, and fitted out a vessel with a steam cylinder on the Newcomen principle which worked a beam and connecting rod to the paddle crankshaft. There were seven paddles on each side of the boat, making 18 strokes a minute. But at the first

26

trials in June 1793 down the Sankey Canal to Newton a speed of only about two miles per hour was achieved. Later, however, his boat steamed to Runcorn and thence down the Duke of Bridgwater Canal to Manchester. There is a story that when Smith was ridiculed for his invention he is said to have replied: 'But before 20 years are over, you will see the Mersey covered with smoke'—a prophecy which was not too inaccurate.

To William Lyttleton, a London merchant, must go the credit, too, for one of the earliest experiments in marine screw propulsion. In 1794 he obtained a patent for what he called an 'aquatic propeller'. This was a triple-threaded screw of a length equal to one complete turn. It was supported in a frame, which could be placed beneath the stern, at the bow, or at the sides. In effect it was not successful, the speed attained when fitted to a small boat being no more than about two miles an hour, but it did push forward, if only by a small amount, the growing knowledge of screw technology. Edward Shorter, another Londoner, also obtained a patent in 1800 for trials of a new method of screw propulsion consisting of a screw with two or more blades which was submerged in the vessel's wake but supported by a buoy to prevent it from sinking too deeply.

As the 19th century dawned the French made a small comeback into the developing technology of the steamboat, in which they had been so prominent 30 or 40 years earlier. M. Desblancs (his Christian name has been lost to posterity) was a watchmaker of Trévoux who devised a paddle-chain steamboat which was tried out on the River Saone but was not a success. It was a shallow flat-bottomed craft, without sails and steered by simple hand tiller. The horizontal double-acting steam cylinder was of cast iron, 21in diameter by 54in stroke and the piston rod was fitted with a double-ratchet mechanism to obtain rotary motion. A transversed shaft behind the cylinder carried chain sprocket-wheels 33in diameter on either side of the boat. The paddle chains also ran on three other pairs of wheels 33in diameter and each carried 30 wooden float boards 33in long and 15in wide. The low-pressure boiler was of oval shape and had an internal furnace about 15in square with internal flues. The outer shell was covered with a wooden barrel and five iron straps.

The first French patent for marine screw propulsion was obtained in 1803 by Charles Dallery of Amiens. One simple screw of two convolutions was fitted at the bow for traction and this could be directed from side to side in order to steer the vessel. Another similar screw was fitted at the stern for propulsion. The two screws were driven by ratchet wheels and endless chains from two vertical steam cylinders of small diameter. He also proposed a boiler with vertical water-tubes and a collapsible tubular funnel. He started work on his steamboat at Bercy, on the River Seine, but his slender finances ran out and he was unable to find a backer.

This brings us to the great Robert Fulton. Frequently glorified as the inventor of the steamboat it is clear that he was preceded by many others, but he nevertheless possessed a rare combination of talents and was not only a gifted artist and draughtsman but a skilled practical mechanic and — perhaps most important of all — a man of shrewd business sense.

As a young man it seemed that he was destined to be an artist: following an early apprenticeship to a jeweller in Philadelphia he began work as a miniature painter and in 1786 came to England to study under Benjamin West, the famous American portrait painter who was then living in this country. He enjoyed an early and quite considerable success but as the years went by began to concern himself more and more with engineering problems. Never a sympathiser with England he in fact gave to the French, then at war with pretty well the whole of Europe, his plans of a submarine to be used against the British blockade. This was the famous *Nautilus* which was launched at Rouen in July 1800. When France lost interest, although the *Nautilus* completed her trials successfully, Fulton turned his attention to the construction of steamboats.

He soon found support from Robert Livingston, the patron of many of the American steamboat pioneers. With Livingston's backing Fulton designed his first experimental steamboat in 1803, which was built in Paris. Unfortunately the hull was structurally unsound and the vessel sank after a storm before its trials. Fulton was able to salvage the machinery and had it fitted in another hull of better construction. The trial eventually took place on 9 August 1803 on the Seine before a great crowd and it steamed up and down for over 90 minutes with two other boats in tow. Upstream a speed of about three miles an hour was attained but this was greatly exceeded when the vessel moved in the opposite direction.

This was encouraging but no more than other men had achieved and in spite of his dislike for the British monarchical system Fulton came back to Britain, visiting Symington in Scotland and studying the machinery of the *Charlotte Dundas*. He also visited the works of Boulton, Watt & Co in Birmingham and found that James Watt's son, who was now running the business, was more enthusiastic than his father about the use of steam power as a means of driving ships. Fulton had no hesitation in ordering the engine for his next boat from what had been described as 'the most experienced engine makers in the world' and in 1806 he returned to America, his new engine following him in a freight vessel.

Livingston encouraged Fulton to build a vessel of 100 tons displacement in the shipyard of Charles Browne on East River, New York. The Boulton & Watt single 24in cylinder engine was installed in the vessel and a copper boiler was made by a local crafts-

Fulton's first
steamboat (1803)

Charlotte Dundas (1801);
Science Museum model

man. It measured 20ft long, 7ft high and 8ft wide and was externally fired. The vessel was driven by two side paddles, each of 15ft diameter and the method of driving the paddles comprised a number of bell cranks, a flywheel and spur gearing. The trials in August 1807 were tolerably successful providing an average speed of about 4.7 miles an hour and aroused tremendous enthusiasm throughout the United States.

It is worth remembering that at this point in history the steamboat, still basically unreliable, had not been even considered as an oceanic vessel; its major opportunity, it was thought, lay in the navigation of rivers

Fulton's *Clermont* (1807)

and canals, especially in areas where the surrounding terrain made transport by stagecoach difficult or hazardous. Conditions such as these abounded in the United States and this explains in some measure the greater interest and success of American inventors of the period when compared with Europe.

Following trials Fulton's vessel, originally known simply as *The Steamboat*, was put on commercial service on the Mississippi later in the same year, when it

became known as *The North River Steamboat*. During the winter of 1807-8 it was temporarily withdrawn from service, refitted and enlarged to 149ft in length, blossoming the next spring with an even longer name: *The North River Steamboat of Clermont*. This was soon shortened to *Clermont* and as such the vessel has passed into immortality. Backed by Livingston no expense had been spared for the winter refit; cabins were added and there was a profusion of gilded and polished woodwork.

The *Clermont* operated on the Hudson for seven years, while Fulton built a series of vessels for Livingston and other steamboat operators. The machinery for all these vessels was made in America and while the designs owed much to the Boulton & Watt beam engine it is obvious that American engineers had made great strides forward in reliability. All Fulton's ventures at this time were highly successful: a decade earlier he had learned a great deal from the study of other people's mistakes and had turned them to his advantage; now, however, he began to make his own original contributions to steamboat technology.

If one cannot credit Fulton with the first practical steamboat he can nevertheless go down in history as the designer and builder of the first steam-driven warship. The *Demologos* was laid down in New York during the war between Britain and the USA and was intended to be used as a coastal defence vessel to break the British blockade. However the war was over before it was completed and although she never saw action there is little doubt she could have done a great deal of damage to the ships of Nelson's navy, especially when becalmed and thus unable to move. The *Demologos* had twenty 32-pounder guns firing red-hot cannon balls which were heated in the boiler furnace. She had a double hull with the paddle-wheels fitted in the intervening space for protection and a bulwark of solid timber 58in thick to protect the main deck. The diameter of her engine cylinder was 48in, twice that of the *Clermont,* and with a 5ft stroke the engine was rated at 120 nominal hp. Unfortunately she was destroyed by an explosion in June 1829.

Another famous Fulton boat was the *Chancellor Livingston*, name in memory of Fulton's sponsor who had died in 1813. The vessel was in service from 1817 to 1834 and Fulton was responsible for the design of the machinery although he himself died before it could be completed. Fulton intoduced a number of innovations in the *Chancellor Livingston* and some of these subsequently became standard practice. For the first time in the United States the boiler furnace was coal-fired instead of wood and the boiler was fitted with internal return flues and two funnels were erected. The engine was a single cylinder 14in diameter with a piston stroke of 5ft which drove two massive 14ft diameter flywheels which in turn transmitted power to the paddles which were themselves 17ft in diameter.

From the beginning the *Chancellor Livingston* set new records and covered the distance from Albany to New York in 18 hours at an average speed of 9.2 miles an hour. At this speed she was a sensation, bearing in mind that this was the immediate pre-railway era.

Before Fulton died the first sea voyage in a steamship had been made — by a man he knew well, John Stevens, who was Livingston's brother-in-law. Although a lawyer by profession, in 1802 Stevens designed and built an entirely new type of marine engine which in fact functioned as a simple turbine. It consisted of a short brass cylinder of 8in bore with a central rotor to which were attached two blades. Steam from a pipe boiler caused the blades to rotate and rotary motion was transmitted by a coupling to a propeller at the stern of the boat. In this invention Stevens was the precursor of later developments in steamboat technology but he failed to overcome the mechanical difficulties — the pipe boiler and the seal-

P.S. Atlantic,
an early American
paddle steamer

ing arrangements for the cylinder ends were never satisfactory — and eventually he abandoned his idea.

His first successful steamship was the *Phoenix* built at Hoboken, New York State. She was launched on 9 April 1808, a flat-bottomed craft with a curved raked stem which carried sails as well as a beam engine. At first she was fitted with two steam cylinders, 16in diameter by 3ft stroke and steam at 3lb per sq in pressure was supplied from a cylindrical boiler with one return flue, set in brickwork. As such she made her sea voyage.

The monopoly for steam navigation on the rivers of New York State had previously been granted to Livingston and thus Stevens decided to despatch the *Phoenix* to Philadelphia by sea. He waited until June 1804 to make sure the weather would be favourable and put the *Phoenix* under the command of Captain Moses Rogers who is said to have entertained very considerable doubts about her seagoing qualities and dropped anchor whenever a slight swell developed. There were also several mechanical breakdowns and so the entire

37

trip took 13 days — a feat of endurance and improvisation.

The first of the American lake steamboats was the *Vermont* built by John and James Winans at Burlington and launched in 1808 for public service on Lake Champlain. The hull was built with a flat bottom and one flush deck. Provision was made for passengers with the cabins below deck but there was no pilothouse and the vessel was steered by hand tiller. She was propelled by a horizontal steam cylinder 20in diameter by 3ft stroke rated at 20 nominal hp and which drove by means of bell-crank side-levers. A flywheel 10ft in diameter carried the machinery over dead centre.

The *Vermont* entered service in June 1809, plying between St Jean, Burlington and Whitehall and made about six miles per hour in favourable weather. On 15 October 1815 she sank in the River Richelieu although her machinery was recovered and sold to the Lake Champlain Steamboat Company who placed it in a new vessel, the *Champlain,* also built by John and James Winans. Then the machinery was removed again and sold to the Lake George Steamboat Company and was used in the steamer *James Caldwell,* the first to run on Lake George, remaining in service until 1820.

Canada at the time had very much the same opportunities and problems as America: an expanding country with many navigable rivers of considerable length running through rough and dangerous country, often without any roads. Thus Canada followed the American developments with close attention and the first Canadian steamboat to be launched was the *Accommodation,* built in Montreal in 1809 by the brewer John Molson, who had emigrated to Canada a few years earlier from Lincolnshire. He had two British partners, John Bruce, a shipbuilder and Captain John Jackson. He went into service on the River St Lawrence in the same year and 'the steamboat receives her impulse from an open, double-spoked perpendicular wheel on each side, without any circular band or rim. To the end of each double spoke is fixed a square board, which enters the water, and by the rotary motion of the wheel acts like a paddle. The wheels are put and kept in motion by steam within the vessel.'

The *Accommodation* left Montreal on her maiden trip under the command of Captain John Jackson and with a French-Canadian river pilot, Amable Laviolette, on 1 November 1809, arriving at Quebec on Saturday 4 November in 66 hours, of which time 30 hours were spent at anchor. Thus she covered the distance of 160 miles at an average speed of 4.45 miles per hour. At the end of her first season she was refitted with a more powerful boiler and began her second season in June 1810 but she does not seem to have been a commercial success.

Far from deterred, Molson launched his second steamboat, the *Swiftsure*, in 1812. She entered service on the St Lawrence in 1813 and made her first scheduled arrival at Quebec on 2 May. She had an average speed of about 7 miles an hour. In 1813 she was chartered to the British for the transport of troops and stores and remained in this service until 1818 when her timbers rotted. The machinery was transferred into another steamboat, the *New Swiftsure*. Molson was responsible for a number of other steamboats and by 1819 the St Lawrence had a reliable, almost daily steamer service.

While the Americas were forging ahead with regular steamboat services Britain, with few rivers and a coastline under constant threat of invasion from Napoleon, had few opportunities for similar development. On the other hand she had developed a steam engine, the motivating force of the Industrial Revolution, and in war as in peace continued to develop the principle.

Watt's patents lapsed in 1800 and immediately a

number of British inventors put forward proposals for improvements. Watt had always been unwilling to use steam at pressures much above atmospheric and his views influenced the early steamboat pioneers, most of whom in any case found it difficult to devise steam-tight boilers even at low pressures. Richard Trevithick was the principal pioneer of the use of high-pressure steam which he had developed particularly for railway locomotion but which could be easily adapted to the needs of the steamship. In 1806 an engine he designed was fitted to operate the dredging machinery of a vessel employed to remove the boulder clay from the entrance of the East India Dock on the Thames at Blackwall. This engine developed about 6hp and was driven by steam at 40lb per sq in — a tremendously high pressure for those days and one which was not used generally until the middle of the century. Trevithick was not alone and in the first decade of the 19th century there was a spate of inventions which were afterwards adopted as standard marine engineering practice.

Matthew Murry stands only second to James Watt in skill as an engine builder. He set up the Round Foundry at Leeds and it was there that he introduced the D-slide valve which was driven off the engine crankshaft; to make this viable he invented a special planing machine to machine its face. He fitted the engines for a steamship which in 1814 began plying between Yarmouth and Norwich and which ran successfully for several years until the boiler exploded in April 1817, resulting in the death of several passengers and crew.

In 1806 Woolf and Edwards opened a factory for constructing steam engines at Lambeth and in 1810 patented what was in fact the first compound engine requiring steam of fairly high pressure. It was not used for steamboats at first but was eventually widely adopted.

Another famous name connected with Lambeth

was Henry Maudslay. He has secured a permanent niche in engineering history for his invention of the slide rest and the screw-cutting lathe — an accurate machine tool incorporating a slide rest, leadscrew and change gears. This invention enabled screw threads to be cut by machine instead of by hand and provided a tremendous boost to steam engine construction. As Maudslay Sons & Field his company became one of the leading marine engine builders of the world and in 1807 he patented his 'table' engine for low power installations and in 1812 a device was patented for blowing air through water on board ship to purify it. Later he invented a boiler feed regulator and a method for preventing the formation of brine in marine boilers.

Another famous name of this time is Henry Bell who as a young man approached the Admiralty in 1803 with plans for steam propulsion based on the results of experiments already carried out. The Admiralty gave him a hearing but after due and weighty consideration could see no merits in steam as a source of power for warships. Inevitably the general introduction of steam would have upset the balance of naval power which at that time existed strongly in Britain's

Bell's *P.S. Comet* (1812)

P.S. Comet (1812);
starboard view
of replica

favour and this was another inhibiting factor for British inventors.

Undeterred Bell, using his own slender resources,
placed an order for a small vessel with John Wood &
Sons of Glasgow. This in fact was the famous *Comet*,
named after Donati's Comet which had appeared earlier that year. The boiler was constructed by Sir John
Napier & Sons of Glasgow at a cost of £27 and was set
in brickwork. David Napier, then a young man in his

twenties, but who was subsequently to become one of the most celebrated of the first generation of Scottish marine engineers, was entrusted with the task of installation. The engine of 4 nominal hp, made by John Robertson of Glasgow is still preserved in the Science Museum in London. It consists of one upright cylinder, 12.5in diameter by 16in stroke, placed over the crankshaft and driving, by means of two side rods, a pair of half side-levers, from which a connecting-rod transmits the power to the overhung crank. The crankshaft carries a balanced flywheel 6ft in diameter and a spur pinion; there is also a single loose eccentric, driven by a pin projecting from the flywheel boss and provided wth two side holes corresponding with the positions for running ahead and astern.

On her trials in August 1812 the *Comet* steamed from Greenock to Glasgow, a distance of about 20 miles, in three hours 30 minutes. News of her impending arrival had spread around the city and she was received with tremendous excitement, the whole riverside being a mass of cheering, waving people. Bell was not slow to act and in the same month advertised her for public service on the Clyde, between Glasgow, Greenock and Helensburgh, leaving Broomielaw on Tuesdays, Thursdays and Saturdays at about midday. To be on the safe side propulsion was quoted as 'by air, wind and steam' and the fare charged was 4s (20p) for the best cabin and 3s (15p) for the second. The 'stinkpot' as the Clyde boatmen called it disdainfully (and which indeed emitted volumes of black smoke from a tall slender funnel) was an immediate success. Originally she was fitted with a pair of paddles each side but it was found that the wash from the forward paddle interfered with the action of its neighbour and a single paddle-wheel was then substituted in place of each pair of radial paddles and at the same time a 12½in cylinder was fitted to the engine. These improvements increased the *Comet's* speed and

Engine of *P.S. Comet*

reduced the journey from Glasgow to Greenock to approximately three hours.

After four years' successful but not particularly economic service on the Clyde Bell took his vessel through the Forth-Clyde Canal and for a short time it operated on the Firth of Forth. In 1819 he established a service to the Western Highlands from Glasgow to Fort William calling at Greenock, Gourock, Rothesay, Tarbet and Oban until, one day in December 1820, while returning from Fort William the *Comet* was wrecked in a storm at Craignash Point, Argyllshire and driven ashore, a total wreck.

The *Comet* was the first steamboat to run a commercial service in Europe: now the idea was catching on fast and even during her short lifetime steamboat services began to appear on the Thames, and on the rivers of Germany and Russia.

2 THE HEROES

By 1815 steamships on the rivers and inland waterways of America, Canada, Britain and Europe were not exactly commonplace but they were no longer the nine days' wonder of a few years earlier. But so far nobody had ventured across the oceans and, said many a bluff sea-dog, retired from the great days under Admiral Lord Nelson, they never would. But they were destined to be proved wrong.

In America there were already numerous steamship companies along the eastern seaboard and on the Mississippi: Bell had shown the way in Britain and Europe, freed from the Napoleonic Wars, was free to spend its new wealth, created by the Industrial Revolution, on innovation and investment. Combined with the growth in capital resources there were technological advances on a broad front, some of which were mentioned in the last chapter.

One of the earliest steamers to follow the *Comet* on

the River Clyde was the *Industry,* built by J & W Fife, famous for their yacht construction, and launched in May 1814. She was stoutly built, with a round bluff bow and high square stern and quarter-deck. Her original side-lever engine had one vertical cylinder 16in diameter by 32in stroke. It had a flywheel and drove the paddle shafts by means of spur wheels; the boiler was made of copper and the funnel served also as a mast. She did service on the Clyde and was refitted in 1828 by Caird & Co Ltd of Greenock with another side-lever engine, remaining in service until 1862 when she was involved in a collision. The cost of the repairs was considered to be unwarranted and she was laid up but the engine was removed to Kelvingrove Museum, Glasgow, where it is still.

A similar vessel, the *Magery,* was also built in Glasgow and launched in 1814. After a short period of service on the Clyde she was sold to Anthony Cortis & Co of London who, however, were not prepared to risk her steaming down the coast. Thus her paddle-wheels were removed and she was towed through the Forth-Clyde Canal and, using her 30ft funnel as a mast, sailed down the East Coast and entered the Thames in 1815. For a season she carried passengers between London and Gravesend and then was sold to a French company. On 17 March 1816 she sailed from Newhaven in a heavy sea to become the first 'steam packet' and the first steamboat to cross the Channel, eventually arriving in Paris on 29 March. She made the voyage under her new name of *Elise.*

The *Thames* was another steamboat to make history. Launched in June 1814 as the *Duke of Argyle* she ran for a short time on the Clyde between Glasgow and Greenock but was sold in April 1815 to R Cheesewright & Company of London who renamed her. She was carvel-built, of oak and fir, fastened with copper and had a square stern and one continuous deck. Her engine was of 14 nominal hp, constructed by James

Cook of Tradeston and she made a speed of six knots — by now the 'knot' had entered into steamship language. Her coal bunkers carried 15 tons and the consumption is said to have been about one ton for 100 miles.

Thames was too wide to pass up the Forth and Clyde Canal and so, under the command of Captain George Dodd, she left Glasgow in the middle of May 1815 with a crew of nine and battled her way at three knots in very rough seas to Dublin. She left on 28 May for Wexford where there was trouble with the paddle-wheels and one float board had to be cut from each. Next *Thames* crossed to Milford Haven and continued round Land's End, the first steam vessel ever to cover those seas. She then steamed up the Channel to London where she arrived on Monday afternoon 12 June — some 758 nautical miles in 122 hours at a mean speed of 6.2 knots. Described as a 'rapid, capacious and splendid vessel' she started service between London and Margate on 3 July 1815 and a year later was transferred to the London — Gravesend service.

London Engineer was the first vessel in England to have the enclosed paddle-wheels which had already been patented by Trevithick and Dickenson in 1808. The vessel was launched in 1818, and was put on the London — Margate run without, however, any great success. The two wheels were arranged in a casing built amidships, air-tight, but open at the bottom, and the floats projected below the floor level to that of the three keels. As the paddle shaft was only about 15in above the water line two air-compressing pumps were provided, which forced air into the casing and thus lowered the water level therein. It was found, however, that the motion of the paddles rapidly carried away the air and the water rose and seriously interfered with the propulsive action of the wheels.

Another famous steamship of the time was *Rob Roy,* the first to establish 'commerce on the open seas'.

Built in 1818 at Dumbarton she maintained a regular steam service between Greenock and Belfast. Then in 1821 she was transferred to the Dover — Calais service and crossed the Channel in about two hours 45 minutes. She was later purchased by the French Government.

By now America, Britain and the French had lost the monopoly in steamships. In 1815 Imperial Russia expressed great interest in this new development and a wooden barge, renamed *Elizabeth*, was rebuilt and engined by a Scotsman, Charles Baird, working at St Petersburg (now Leningrad). The steamer was used on the River Neva, maintaining a daily service between St Petersburg and Kronstadt.

The first steamboat to be built in Prussia was the *Prinzessian Charlotte*, a double-hulled wooden vessel constructed by John Rubie at Dichelsdorf, near Spandau, and launched in 1816. The vessel was intended for use on the Elbe, Havel and Spree rivers and had a side-lever engine constructed by Boulton, Watt & Co. James Watt's company also supplied the side-lever machinery and boiler for *Die Weser* built near Bremen the following year. A number of other steamers were later built at Potsdam and fitted with engines supplied by the same firm.

The first steamer in the Mediterranean was *Ferdinando Primo,* built at Naples and launched on 24 June 1818. She was a three-masted vessel with the paddle-wheels placed well forward. She had 16 private cabins and a public saloon for 50 persons forward. The side-lever machinery was of British construction. *Ferdinando Primo* sailed from Naples in October 1818 under the command of Captain Andrea di Martino and arrived to the sound of a brass band and vast cheering crowds at Genoa on 28 October. She left Genoa on 30 October with 10 passengers and arrived at Marseilles on 3 November, the first steam vessel ever to be seen in that port.

P.S. Savannah c. 1819

With the advent of the coastal 'hops' of the early steamships around Britain and the first cross-Channel steamers the heroic age can truly be said to have dawned. Voyages at the mercy of the unpredictable sea are never commonplace even in these days, but 150 years ago it required real heroism to cross the Irish Sea or even the Channel in a tiny boat powered by an unreliable source of propulsion.

However, these exploits paled into insignificance when, in 1819 *Savannah* crossed the Atlantic. She was built of wood at Corlers Hook, New York, by one Francis Fickett and launched on 22 August 1818. At first she was intended for sail-packet service to Le Havre, France but before she was completed she was purchased by the newly formed Savannah Steamship Co and adapted for auxiliary steam propulsion with collapsible paddle-wheels. To aid her considerable spread of sail she was fitted with an auxiliary steam engine of 90 hp, constructed by Stephen Vail at the Speedwell Ironworks near Morristown, New Jersey. This engine had one cylinder 40in diameter by 5ft stroke, which was inclined at about 20^0 so as to act directly on to the paddle shaft. The steam inlet and exhaust pipes were of equal bore because there was no expansion in the cylinder and the steam was discharged hot and at full pressure to the jet condenser. The air pump for this condenser worked on the same cross-head as the main piston rod. Steam was supplied by low pressure boilers with riveted flues and the pressure is said to have been less than 1lb per sq in above atmospheric. These boilers had to be blown out once a day to avoid salt-water concentration. The paddle-wheels were over 15ft in diameter but were made to be collapsible so that they could be taken on deck when not in use.

By the time she was finished and her trials had been completed the Savannah Steamship Company was experiencing a recession of business and it was decided to send her to Europe for sale. She was widely advertised as sailing for Liverpool with an intermediate call at New York 'should a sufficient number of passengers offer' but in fact none chose to participate in her fame and her proposed call at New York was cancelled.

Savannah finally left her home port on 24 May 1819, bound direct for Liverpool and under the command of Captain Moses Rogers who had already commanded the *Phoenix*, the first steamboat on the open sea. As there were no passengers she stowed 75 tons of coal and 25 cords of wood. She persevered across the Atlantic, under sail mostly but aided occasionally by her paddles and made an average speed of about six knots. On 17 June she was seen off the coast of Ireland and reported to be a ship on fire. The following day her log book contains the laconic entry: 'no cole to git up steam'.

She put in at Kinsale for coal and steamed on to Liverpool, where she arrived on 20 June. *The Times* noted: 'The *Savannah,* a steam vessel, recently arrived at Liverpool from America, the first vessel of the kind which ever crossed the Atlantic, was chased the whole day off the coast of Ireland by the *Kite*, revenue cruiser on the Cork station, which mistook her for a ship on fire.' The crossing from Savannah had taken 27 days 11 hours and her paddle-wheels were used on seven occasions, for a total of only 85 hours and only when there was so little wind that her speed would have been otherwise severely restricted.

From Liverpool *Savannah* set forth to Elsinore, thence to Stockholm and then on to St Petersburg where it was hoped to sell her to Tsar Alexander I. Unsuccessful, her Captain was ordered to return to the United States on 22 October. She sailed to her home port from Arendal, Norway—under sail because of the high cost of coal in Europe.

Although she had crossed and re-crossed the Atlantic nobody at the time seemed very impressed and there was little or no comment in the contemporary press about the possibilities opened up by trans-oceanic travel by steamship. Perhaps it was because she was a hybrid, whereas the river steamers were depending entirely on steam for their progress.

On 3 December 1819 the Savannah Steamship Co, now rather desperate financially and even more out of pocket by the abortive voyage to Europe, sent her to Washington in the hope that the US Government might purchase her. But nothing came of this and in 1820 she was sold at auction. Her engines were taken out and she became a coastal sail-packet between Savannah and New York, finally running aground on Long Island in a gale in 1821 and becoming a total wreck.

Although the United States can claim the first steam crossing of the Atlantic by the eastern route Britain claims the first crossing of the Atlantic westwards, for although *Savannah* certainly went back to the States she did so under sail alone.

The first authenticated steamship crossing of the Atlantic from east to west was made in 1821-2 by the first British steam warship, the *Rising Star*, which had originally been ordered in 1818 by Thomas Cochrane for use as a steam warship in the Chilean Revolution. However she was ready too late and did not run her trials until June 1821, on the Thames. She finally sailed from Gravesend on 22 October, bound for Valparaiso, but sprang a leak off the coast of Portugal and put into port for repairs. She eventually arrived at Valparaiso in April 1822, the first steamer to enter the Pacific. However, *Rising Star*, like *Savannah*, was a hybrid and her twin-cylinder only aided a considerable spread of sail.

As the first great age of steamship heroism developed and the little ships went out across the seas to create sensations wherever they docked, there was increased activity on the drawing boards, in the shipyards and the engineering plants. Until about 1815 the majority of engineers were involved in the problem of making really efficient steam engines which did not leak or explode and which kept running. Now, the basics fairly well established, it was possible to contemplate refinements.

The shipyards, too, were looking at new concepts. The early steamboats all looked like sailing ships with funnels stuck on them but it was soon realised that a steam-propelled vessel behaved differently at sea from a sailing ship and thus called for a different design approach. For example, with an engine there was no need to tack and the inherent tendency of a sailing hull to heel was a definite disadvantage to the efficient working of the paddles. Gradually the shipbuilders altered the shape of their steamships. The bows were fined down, the stern became less stumpy and the midship section less square. One of the pioneers in this work was David Napier who in 1818 began to experiment with model ships and even carried out tests in a specially constructed tank not so very different from those used today to assess hull performance. David Napier was soon established as a leader of the first generation of Scots marine engineers—a position shared, perhaps, by his cousin Robert who was only a year younger. Robert Napier was first apprenticed as a blacksmith and then afterwards he obtained a position at an engine works in Edinburgh. Later he set up in business on his own and his first engine was built in 1823 and fitted into the steamship *Leven*, which subsequently operated a regular service on the Clyde between Glasgow and Dumbarton. The engine was of the familiar side-lever type, a modified form of the Watt beam engine which Napier developed to a greater degree than any other engine builder. The *Leven* engine represented a high point in Scottish engineering and remained in service for a remarkably long time. In 1845 when the *Leven* was removed from service the engine was fitted to another vessel, *Merlin* which continued to operate until 1856. That year *Merlin* was damaged in a storm and laid up but the engine was not removed until 1877 when it was presented to Dumbarton by the Napier family and is still preserved today, at the foot of Dumbarton rock, as a memorial to Robert Napier. Napier's already considerable reputation was enhanced in 1827 when two vessels fitted with his engines beat all comers in a steamboat race on the Clyde; by 1830 he was recognised as one of the leading marine engine builders in Britain.

In the south, Maudslay's of Lambeth had already created a considerable reputation for themselves and were soon joined by John Penn of Greenwich who made his first engine for the paddle steamer *Ipswich*, which operated a service between London and Norwich beginning in 1825. Like Maudslay's, Penn's company was a family firm and his sons joined the business to carry the firm through the 19th century as one of the leaders of the Thames engineering and shipbuilding industry. Another early, outstanding engineer in steamship technology was John Seaward who established the Canal Ironworks at Millwall and constructed the engine for the *Royal George*, designed for the Dover — Calais service.

Yet another celebrated partnership was that of Miller and Barnes. Joseph Miller invented a direct-acting paddle engine which took up less room than the standard side-lever engine which itself had replaced Watt's beam engine as being too unwieldy for steamships.

For the time being, however, there was little inclination to investigate the possibilities of trans-oceanic travel by steamship—perhaps because there was too much money to be made immediately, both in America and in Britain, by the less adventurous, less risky river trips.

In America, in spite of the beginnings of the early

56

railroads, steamship travel had established itself as a viable and necessary means of communication; in Britain, however, it was chiefly exploited as a means of pleasure—a day out on the water. In the 1820s about 30 steamboats were on regular service on the Thames and for the first time in history voyages could be enjoyed by large cross-sections of the public. Services were established down-river from London to as far as Margate, stopping at Woolwich, Gravesend, Southend and Sheerness on the way. They were responsible more than anything else for the transformation of Margate from a small fishing village at the beginning of the 19th century to a town of over 11,000 people by 1844, two years before the railway arrived. Just as pleasure steamers go out now from Hungerford Pier near Charing Cross Station, so they did 150 years ago.

Activities such as these led to the formation of the first of the 'lines'. The famous General Steam Navigation Company was formed in 1824 by a number of London merchants who owned small steam packets operating between London and Margate. This company is today the oldest sea-going steamship company in operation. The nucleus of the company's first fleet was 12 wooden steam packets purchased between the years 1824 and 1828. Among them was the original *Eagle*, the forerunner of a long line of steamships called by the same name and which are still associated with pleasure cruising on the Thames between London and Margate; to this day an *Eagle* does the trip throughout the summer months.

Steamships were also responsible for opening up Scotland and making possible regular connections with the Isles. The Glasgow Castles Steam Packet Company, the Laird Line and the Glasgow and Londonderry Steam Packet Company were all formed in 1814/5. A regular service was begun between Belfast and Liverpool in 1819, about which time regular services were established to the Western Isles.

In 1825 a British-built steamboat made history in a more heroic style when the *Enterprise* made a journey out to India under steam and sail. She left Falmouth on 16 August and reached Calcutta on 7 December, a total of 113 days, of which 64 were under steam.

The ship was fitted with a large copper boiler which steamed on seawater. This method of operation created a major problem for the early steamships which had to stop frequently so that salt could be cleared from the boilers, an operation which entailed a heavy consumption of coal at a time when coaling stations were far apart. However, the *Enterprise* had a recently patented system, devised by Maudslay Sons & Field, of pumping the hot brine out of the boiler and using it to heat the incoming feedwater. This scheme saved some coal and more importantly considerably reduced the need to blow down the boiler, although it was not until the 1830s that a practical surface condenser was invented which could supply the boilers with fresh water and bring about a substantial saving in the coal used on a long voyage. In spite of Maudslay's system there is no doubt that *Enterprise* was under sail on many days when she need not have been if it had been possible for her to carry sufficient coal to steam.

After the voyage Ash, the chief engineer, wrote a report to Maudslay's regarding the performance of the machinery, mostly confined to listing minor defects such as broken brass bolts and broken valve spindles which were repaired by the crew. Unfortunately the steamship captains of those early days had to rely on copper-zinc alloy brass which does not possess a very high tensile strength and the special-purpose bronzes such as manganese and phosphor bronze were not introduced until the latter part of the 19th century. Another problem which the *Enterprise* had to face was associated with the boilers; leaky joints were a constant source of trouble particularly when first filled with water—so much so that a common trick was to add oatmeal, the idea being that the oatmeal swelled and stopped the leaks.

The *Enterprise* remained out East for many years and continued to use her engine whenever fuel was available.

As steamships became slowly more efficient it was not surprising that more and more inventors and engineers should try to interest the Admiralty in the potential for steam power. As we have seen the Earl of Stanhope and John Hulls had already tried without much success. Now it was the turn of Marc Brunel, who became one of the leading advocates of steam warships for auxiliary purposes. He first interested the Admiralty in a steamship for 'parking' purposes and in 1819 a steamship, *Eclipse* towed *HMS Hastings*, a ship of the line, from London to two miles beyond Gravesend against a rising tide. This encouraged the Admiralty to order a small steamboat as a harbour tug and in 1822 *HMS Comet*, the first steam-driven fighting ship of the Royal Navy was launched at Deptford. Her engine was built by Maudslay's who were also responsible for *HMS Lightning* which was launched the following year. In 1824 she made history by being the first steam warship in the Royal Navy to go into action—against the Algerian pirates on the Barbary Coast.

While steam now had a foot in the Admiralty door there was no fundamental change of policy: sail and the ability to handle it better than any other nation on earth made it the first choice of the British Navy. For many years steamships in the Royal Navy were engaged on menial tasks towing ships of the line into harbour or delivering mail to British possessions.

The Admiralty Lords' objection to steam was not entirely unfounded. In the 30s of the last century working pressures, which were still only a few pounds above atmospheric, meant that the engines were grossly inefficient and coal consumption was enormous in relation to the power obtained. On a long voyage it was possible to spend nearly a third of the time coaling in harbours. Another objection to the use of steam in warships was that the engines were vulnerable and could not be protected by being placed below the water line because they were too bulky. Maudslay Sons & Field countered by producing the 'Siamese engine' which comprised two pairs of single-acting cylinders that were usually placed fore and aft under the paddle shaft.

P.S. Curacao

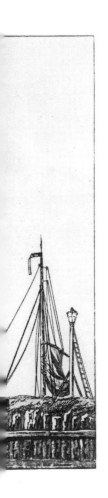

Despite these and many other problems a new breed of men, steamship captains and engineers, were coming into existence. Long voyages continued, although as yet none was completed entirely under steam. In 1824 the French steam warship *Caroline* sailed from Brest to Cayenne in French Guiana and the *Curaçao* made three return trips to the Dutch West Indies between 1827 and 1829. Another early voyage to the West Indies was by the British warship *HMS Rhadamanthus*, the first steam vessel to be built at Devonport dockyard and subsequently the first steam vessel of the Royal Navy to cross the Atlantic, making the journey from Plymouth to Barbados via Madeira in 27 days.

The question now was, 'Could a vessel carry sufficient coal to complete the Atlantic crossing under steam alone— bearing in mind that it might have to face adverse winds and seas for 3,000 miles?' In part, this question was answered in 1833 by the successful west to east crossing of the Canadian steamship *Royal William*. She made her voyage entirely under steam, except for periods when the boilers shut down for descaling, which took considerable time about 24 hours every fourth day. In these circumstances it is not surprising that the voyage from Nova Scotia to Cowes, Isle of Wight, should have taken 18 days. The *Royal William* was built in 1831 in Quebec and her twin-lever engines of 200 nominal hp were supplied by Bennet and Henderson of Montreal; the crankshafts, which were too large for any forge in Canada, were supplied by Robert Napier's works at Govan. *Royal William* was later sold to the Spanish Government and became the warship *Isabella Segunda*.

Now an outstanding man enters the story of the steamship: Isambard Kingdom Brunel, chief engineer of the Great Western Railway Company. Earlier he had been chief engineer for the excavations of the Blackwall Tunnel when, with his father, Marc Brunel,

Royal West India
Mail Company Fleet in
Southampton Water

he had devised a tunnelling shield which became the prototype for tunnel equipment used to this day. He was also the designer of the suspension bridge across the Avon Gorge at Bristol and the architect of the railway between London and Bristol.

At a meeting of the Great Western Railway Company in October 1835—when Brunel was still only 29—the proposal to build a steamship was first discussed. The historic meeting took place at Radleys Hotel, Blackfriars in London. One of the directors carped about the enormous length of the main line the company was building to Bristol and Brunel, dead pan, suggested it should be extended to New York by means of a steamship plying between Bristol and America. Such was their faith in this remarkable man that the directors set up a separate company, the Great Western Steamship Company, the first concern to be formed with the specific purpose of engaging in passenger transport across the Atlantic by steamship. News of the company's formation sharpened the coal versus power versus storage space controversy which had been going on for several years. The antis had a remarkably simple case—on the face of it. They pointed out that if the size of a hull was doubled to increase the coal-capacity the vessel would require double the power to drive it and the coal consumption would also be doubled. Thus no matter how large a vessel was built it would still consume all its fuel before it could complete the journey, particularly when travelling east-west and subject to adverse winds. Brunel's answer was simple but convincing: while the carrying capacity of a hull increased as the cube of its dimensions, its resistance, or the power required to drive it through the water, only increased as the square of those dimensions. Brunel took delight in pointing out that his critics lacked basic engineering knowledge.

Building of Brunel's ship began in the Bristol shipyard of William Patterson. Brunel had never designed

The *Great Western*

a ship before yet his remarkable understanding of materials and appreciation of the forces involved led him to assess and overcome all the difficulties swiftly and surely. His hull was built on ribs of oak but he achieved longitudinal strength to resist the fury of the Atlantic waves by four staggered rows of iron bolts which ranged the entire length of the ship throughout the bottom frames. Also, an innovation for commercial craft, he enclosed the hull in a sheath of copper below the water line. Maudslay Sons and Field supplied the engine—the largest built at the Lambeth works up to that time but of the standard side-lever design with twin cylinders 73.5in diameter by 7ft stroke. Steam was supplied at a pressure of 5lb per sq in from four return-flue iron boilers, each having three furnaces.

Considering her size and specification *Great Western* was launched in record time—on 19 July 1837 —and a month later she made the journey round the South Coast of England under sail to the Thames to take on her engines.

Apart from engineering sophistication she was the most luxurious steamship yet constructed. The main feature was her passenger saloon, 75ft long and 21ft wide, complemented by berths for 120 first class passengers and 20 second class.

Brunel's venture attracted enormous attention and sparked off the whole idea of ocean-going steamship travel which had been debated for so long. Brunel's name was a guarantee of success and it was realised that if *Great Western* succeeded she would have an unchallenged monopoly. Overnight other companies were formed to compete on the route and two serious challengers appeared before *Great Western* had been completed. They were the British and American Steam Navigation Company of London and the Transatlantic Steamship Company of Liverpool. British and American lost no time in laying down a vessel that was slightly larger than Brunel's ship. Named *British Queen* she had a figurehead of Queen Victoria. Work on *British Queen* went on day and night but when it

S.S. Royal William
c. 1833

became evident that Brunel had too great a lead the company abandoned their plans and negotiated for the hire of a steamer, *Sirius*, which had been built a year before for service between London and Cork.

The Transatlantic Steamship Company were also forced to charter and they went for *Royal William*, a steamer built for the Irish cross-channel service but which should not be confused with the Canadian-built ship mentioned earlier. This *Royal William* was even smaller than *Sirius* and in fact became the smallest passenger ship ever to steam the whole distance from Europe to America, as well as the first Atlantic steamship to sail from Liverpool.

By the early spring of 1838 shipbuilders and engineers were confident that the only two contestants were *Sirius* and *Great Western*. *Royal William*, even if she sustained the course, could never hope to compete timewise.

The forthcoming contest between *Sirius* and *Great Western* was, as one might expect, likened to the contest of David and Goliath. The gross registered tonnage of *Sirius* was only 703 tons compared with 1,320 of *Great Western*. Brunel's engines were over twice as powerful and perhaps most important of all was the fact that despite the disparity in sizes the coal consumption of *Sirius* was 80% that of *Great Western* although her bunker capacity was a great deal less. Generally the odds were weighted heavily against *Sirius* who might well complete the voyage but, it was thought, would have to do so under sail.

Sirius had only one advantage: she was ready first and able to leave London on 28 March 1838 when *Great Western* was still undergoing trials in the Thames. *Great Western* was further delayed by a small fire which occurred in the boiler room due to the ignition of some lagging. There was much confusion and Brunel who was on board fell and was injured when going to investigate the cause. The ship's captain,

P.S. Sirius c. 1838

Lieutenant James Hosken RN, thought the disaster was more serious than it turned out to be and headed the vessel towards Canvey Island where she was put aground. *Great Western* was refloated on the evening tide without mishap and she went on to Bristol, arriving safely on 2 April. But news of the fire had preceded her and 50 of the 57 passengers who had booked for the voyage cancelled. Then the weather took a hand: after taking on coal and stores she was ready to sail on 7 April but she was delayed by a storm and it was not until the Sunday, 8 April that she was able to get away. Meanwhile *Sirius*, with 40 passengers aboard, had taken on coal at Cork and left on 4 April for New York. Thus *Sirius* was four days ahead although bets were still laid on *Great Western* because of her superior speed.

Indeed *Sirius* encountered strong headwinds in mid-Atlantic and some of the passengers and crew urged the captain to turn back. But her master, Lieutenant Roberts RN, carried on and although coal began to run short after about 3,000 miles a full head of steam was maintained until the vessel anchored off New York harbour on 22 April. The crossing had taken 18 days 10 hours and there were just 15 tons of coal left in the bunker.

Great Western, not surprisingly, bettered *Sirius's* time, as everyone had expected, arriving in the early hours of 23 April with a crossing time of 15 days 5 hours, but the fact remained that *Sirius* was there by a short head. However, *Great Western* had 200 tons of coal still in her bunker and this convinced America more than anything else that a new era of speedy and reliable ocean transport had arrived. Both ships received a tremendous welcome, not from thousands of people lining the harbour walls but by hundreds of small ships which put out from shore to greet the heroes.

Great Western had no problems at all in booking 70 passengers on her return journey and she again made the crossing in 15 days in spite of an engine being out of action for 48 hours with a broken connecting rod. It is said that her arrival at the mouth of the Avon was greeted with an enthusiasm not seen since the news of the victories at Trafalgar and Waterloo a generation earlier.

Nor was *Great Western's* feat just a flash in the pan. Like all Brunel's creations—and the creations of most of the engineers of the 19th century—she was built for consistent reliability. She continued to ply between Bristol and New York, crossing the North Atlantic 64 times during the eight years between 1838 and 1846. In 1847 she was sold to the Royal Mail Steam Packet Co Ltd and for 10 years operated a regular service between Southampton and the West Indies, until she was finally broken up at Vauxhall in 1857.

But *Great Western* was more than a record breaker: she represented a notable advance in steamship construction. The longitudinal strengthening of the hull

P.S. Sirius (1837); model

P.S. President (1839)

was an innovation subsequently copied by many other designers and the size and power output of her engines, although of orthodox design, became standard for the first generation of transatlantic vessels.

As we have seen Britain lost ground to America in the early development of the steamship; at one stroke Brunel put Britain back as a leader in what was to prove to be the most lucrative passenger shipping route in the world right up until the development of the jet aircraft. Fulton had put America in the lead; Brunel snatched it back for Britain.

Sirius made only one more trip to America before returning to her original role as an Irish packet; her career was cut short in January 1847 when she ran on to a reef of rocks in Ballycotton Bay and became a total loss. *British Queen*, which had been temporarily abandoned by the British and American Steam Navigation Company, became her successor and sailed on the first Atlantic crossing from Portsmouth on 12 July 1839, completing the voyage in 15 days. Her hull construction was similar to that of Brunel's and she imitated, too, his standards of luxury accommodation for passengers. She crossed to America nine times before being sold to the Belgian Government in 1841 and then continued on the North Atlantic run for her new owners, operating between New York and Antwerp. Unfortunately technical success is not always profitable and the Transatlantic Steamship Company was wound up in July 1840 when many of the company's vessels were sold to the Peninsular and Oriental Steam Navigation Company. The Great Western Steamship Company went out of business in 1847 and the British and American Steam Navigation Company suffered a considerable loss of confidence, and thus of revenue, when their *President*, a sister ship to the *British Queen* sank in an Atlantic gale on 11 March 1841 with 163 persons on board. Her captain, Lieutenant Roberts RN, the former captain of the *Sirius*, went down with her. This was the first steamship to be lost in the Atlantic service.

The British and North American Royal Mail Steam Packet Company became the successor to the British

P.S. Hibernia (1842); an early Cunard ship

and American and later changed its name to the Cunard Steamship Company. Perhaps it was saved by the fact that Samuel Cunard, the founder, was a good enough businessman to obtain a contract from the General Post Office to carry the mail between Britain and North America. With this bread and butter contract in his pocket he ordered four ships from various builders on the Clyde and used them to establish a monthly steamship mail service between Liverpool, Halifax and Boston. The engines for Cunard's first four ships were ordered from Robert Napier and indeed Napier provided all the engines for Cunard's paddle steamers from 1840 until 1855.

3
THE
IRON SHIPS

In spite of the success of the *Great Western*, considerable limitations were imposed on the development of the steamship at this time. In 30 years significant advances had been made but they were advances of refinement rather than of fundamental principles. Wooden hulls, paddle-wheels and single-cylinder engines with jet condensers all meant that although the steamship engineers and shipbuilders were working to the best of their abilities they did so with certain inherent limitations.

Between 1840 and 1870 the gradual replacement of wooden ships by iron, the introduction of the screw propeller and the use of the compound engine with surface condensers transformed the situation.

The first recorded iron hull construction in Britain dates back to 1777, when a small pleasure boat was made of sheet iron on the banks of the River Fosse in Yorkshire; it was 12ft long and 6ft wide. Ten years later an iron canal boat named *Trial,* of about 40 tons loaded displacement, was built by a John Wilkinson at Willey in Shropshire; it was 70ft long and 6.7ft wide. The hull plates were 0.312in thick and were secured with rivets; but the stem and stern posts were made of wood and the gunwales were lined with wood, the beams being made of elm planks. In 1809 Trevithick and Dickenson obtained a patent for an iron ship construction, which specified that the decks as well as the hulls should be made of iron plates, but there is no record of it having been built.

The first commercial vessel to be constructed entirely of iron was *Vulcan*, built by Thomas Wilson at Faskine, Scotland in 1818 and designed for canal use. The hull was 63ft long, 13ft wide and 5ft deep, built of iron plates on flat bar frames, all the frames and stanchions being forged by hand. As an aftermath of the Napoleonic Wars timber suitable for ship construction was at a premium and naval architects were, without much enthusiasm, forced to consider the use of iron although many experienced shipbuilders declared that it was a practice 'contrary to Nature'.

The first steamboat to be constructed of iron was laid down in 1821 and was the *Aaron Manby,* built by Aaron Manby, a Tipton, Staffordshire iron master and his eldest son, Charles Manby. Consultant engineer for the project was Captain (later Admiral Sir) Charles Napier who had involved himself with a company to promote the use of iron steamers on the River Seine. The hull was constructed of iron plates 0.25in thick with a flat bottom and square stern. The fore-and-aft seams were lapped and riveted and the ribs consisted of angle iron. However, the keelson was of wood and wooden bearers were provided under the engines. The deck and the beams which supported it were also of wood. *Aaron Manby* was decked in from end to end to protect her cargo from the weather and it was also claimed from fire, a scourge of the early steamships.

In the same year as he built his ship Aaron Manby took out a patent for a marine oscillating engine, apparently unaware that William Murdoc, one of Watt's solicitors, had proposed the idea of an oscillating engine as early as 1785 and that a patent had actually been granted to a Mr Witty in 1811. Nevertheless Manby was the first to build an engine operating on the oscillating principle.

Steam at low pressure (it is thought not more than about 2lb per sq in above atmospheric) was supplied from two flat-sided iron boilers placed side by side. Each boiler contained two furnaces with return flues. At first Manby intended to use two pairs of paddle-wheels but the plans were modified later and *Aaron Manby* was fitted with a single pair of 12ft diameter.

When the hull was finished it was transported in sections to London and assembled at the Surrey Docks, Rotherhithe. Trials were run on the Thames between Battersea and Blackfriars in May 1822 and *The London Courier* said that the vessel 'is the most complete specimen of workmanship in the iron way that has ever been witnessed, and draws one foot less water than any steamboat that has ever been built'. In June 1822 she left the Thames with a cargo of linseed and iron, crossed the Channel to Le Havre and proceeded up the River Seine to Paris where many of the inhabitants thought she was a fake because iron could never float. Nevertheless she was the first iron-built vessel that ever put to sea and the first vessel to proceed from London direct to Paris.

Another similar iron steamer, *Commerce de Paris* of 130 tons was built in 1823 at the Horsely Ironworks. She could not steam to France, however, because of new import restrictions and she was thus shipped in sections and re-assembled at Charenton, near Paris, where Aaron Manby had founded the ironworks of Manby, Wilson, Henry et Cie. Two further iron steamers were later constructed at Charenton and went into regular service on the Seine. During her career on the river *Aaron Manby* ran aground several times but no serious damage was sustained and she never needed repairs to her iron hull. In 1830 she was sold and in 1836 was at Nantes in service on the River Loire. She was not broken up until 1855.

The success of *Aaron Manby* received considerable publicity, both in the press generally and more particularly among shipbuilders. But it did not lead to the immediate adoption of iron for ships' hulls and there was an inherent resistance to an innovation which cut right across the traditional shipbuilding techniques; as one might expect such resistance was particularly strong in Britain who had built up her world-wide power on the basis of her 'wooden walls'. Nevertheless Britain was also the leader of the Industrial Revolution and the production of wrought iron in Britain was increasing rapidly and the price of iron plate was falling steadily; even 130 years ago Britain had been largely deforested, so that necessity if nothing else began to favour the use of iron.

By the 1830s iron steamboats had become fairly common for short haulage work but nobody had yet dared to put one forward for ocean-going vessels. One early deterrent was that Lloyds refused to classify iron ships for insurance purposes. William Fairbairn, who owned a shipyard at Millwall, London finally altered this by improving the techniques used in the construction of iron ships to such an extent that they were accepted.

Fairbairn was one of a long line of designers who tried to persuade the Admiralty to use iron, but had no more success than his predecessors. This is not really surprising because his experiments in this direction were an outstanding failure. He experimented in front of some of the Admiralty Lords by firing a 32lb shot at targets representing the side of an iron ship, but unfortunately the shot penetrated both single and double thicknesses of ½in and ⅝in plates so their Lordships went away unimpressed.

As the 40s dawned however, iron ships, had a size-able number of devotees among the experts. Improving iron technology enhanced their case: some of the new rolling mills were able to handle larger plates, thus reducing bolting and welding. Once again Isambard Brunel proved to be the man of vision that was needed. He persuaded the Great Western Steamship Company to build another ship that would be even larger and faster than *Great Western*. Brunel determined that it should be an iron ship and plans were drawn up and keel plates laid in Bristol on 19 July 1839. The keel was made of flat plate 0.88in thick and 20in wide, fire-welded into lengths of 50 — 60ft and subsequently scarf jointed and riveted. The outside plates were around 6ft long and 3ft wide with a thickness ranging from 0.38 to 0.69. Five transverse bulkheads divided the ship into six watertight compartments, each connected with the bilge pumps, and further strength was given by two longitudinal bulkheads which divided the vessel up to main deck level.

Unfortunately there were delays in relation to the engines: the Great Western Steamship Company disregarded Brunel's advice to use Maudslay's, who had served them so well for the *Great Western,* and instead a young man, Francis Humphys, was appointed engineer-in-charge of the project, which the company decided to undertake themselves. At first there were difficulties in manufacturing the paddle shaft which was so large that it was impossible to forge with the standard drop hammers in use at the time. Finally James Nasmyth, an engineer of Patricroft, near Manchester, came to the rescue and designed a power hammer operated by steam, far more powerful than any of those already in existence. But although the paddle shaft was successfully forged it was never installed in the vessel because towards the end of 1850 Brunel

*S.S. Great Britain
at Port Stanley in
the Falklands c. 1905*

decided that the *Great Britain* should not only be the first iron steamship on the Atlantic but it should also be the first to adopt the screw propeller. Francis Humphys who had spent so much time and anxiety over the design of his engines threw up his hands in despair. In fact he had a nervous breakdown and very shortly afterwards died of what the medics of the time diagnosed as 'brain fever'.

Nothing daunted, Brunel carried on: several different propeller designs were proposed and several reached the production stage, one being a six-bladed propeller of 16ft diameter made as a single casting. But this was rejected and ultimately a slightly smaller screw of 15½ft diameter made in sections from wrought iron was used. This also had six blades, each of which was 6in thick and riveted on to a central boss. The engines, which were totally re-designed, now comprised four inclined cylinders 88in diameter and 72in stroke. Steam was generated at about 15lb per sq in — a high pressure of the time and three times greater than that used for the *Great Western*.

79

With all these innovations it was nearly four years from the laying of the first plates until the vessel was launched by the Prince Consort on 19 July 1843. Preliminary fitting took place at Bristol and sea trials were held in the following year, when a speed of 11 knots was reached. In January 1845 the *Great Britain* sailed round to the Thames for the final fitting up and decoration of the main saloon which, as in the case of *Great Western,* was a special feature.

At Blackwall, where she lay at anchor, she aroused considerable interest and thousands flocked to see her. Queen Victoria herself visited the vessel which remained there for a year before setting out, on 26 July 1846, on her maiden voyage from Liverpool to New York with 60 passengers and 600 tons of cargo. Her first crossing was completed in 14 days 21 hours and the return journey in 15½ days. However, on her second trip the propeller was damaged and the voyage had to be completed under sail. Brunel, innovator though he was, would never have dreamed of designing a steamship without sails which could be used in an emergency and it was incidents of this kind which made many in naval and commercial circles alike unwilling to abandon sail altogether. The repair to her propeller did not detain her for long and she was soon back on the Atlantic run, this time with modified boilers which reduced her average voyage to 13 days.

Then, at the height of her success disaster struck. She left Liverpool on 22 September 1846 with 180 passengers, the largest number ever to be carried on a transatlantic steamship. The next morning Brunel and his directors received the bad news by telegraph: the most powerful steamship yet built was aground in Dundrum Bay, Co Down.

At the subsequent enquiry the catastrophe was attributed to new charts which had been published for the area and which were faulty, although Brunel also suspected that the massive amount of iron in the ship

The *Persia*

could have affected the performance of the compass. Several attempts were made to refloat the vessel without success and the passengers were taken off. Ever inventive, Brunel devised a protective breakwater round her stern and exposed quarter to protect her from the prevailing south-westerly winds. The breakwater consisted of 8,000 faggots skewered together with iron rods and this was so effective that she sustained no damage during the 11 months she was stranded at Dundrum Bay. This was not only a tribute to Brunel's capacity for improvisation but, more to the point, of his construction methods and of the principle of building in iron. Even with the breakwater it is doubtful that a wooden ship would have survived at all.

In August 1847 *Great Britain* was successfully refloated and towed to Liverpool for repairs which could have been carried out relatively easily. But it was too late: the disaster had ruined the company and both the *Great Western* and the *Great Britain* were sold.

Thereafter this ship had a remarkable record of service on the Liverpool — Melbourne route for many years as an auxiliary-screw steamer. Then in 1882 her machinery was removed but she remained in active service as a sailing vessel until 1886 when she was damaged in a storm off Cape Horn. Later still she was in service as a coal hulk until October 1937, when she was finally beached at Sparrow Cove, Port William.

Slowly the iron age was coming. Cunard held out for a long time but in 1855 ordered their first iron paddle steamer, *Persia*. It was built by Robert Napier, who followed Brunel's precept of insisting on maximum longitudinal strength and the internal sub-division of the hull into watertight compartments — seven in the case of this ship. Accommodation was provided for 250 passengers and in July 1856 she crossed from Liverpool to New York in nine days one hour 45 min at an average speed of 13.82 knots, thereby claiming the Blue Riband, which she held until 1862.

By 1846 the Royal Navy had 16 iron warships with a further nine in the course of construction, but only four of these vessels were over 1,000 tons. In the Crimean War it was noted that the French fleet supporting the army off Sebastopol suffered heavily at the hands of the Russian shore batteries until the ships were protected with iron armour. This lesson was confirmed in 1861 by the outbreak of the American Civil War. The Confederates lost no time in armouring the *Merrimac* which was lying at Norfolk Navy Yard. Ten 7in rifled guns were located within this armament, firing through holes in the structure and a heavy metal ram was fastened to the bow. On 8 March 1862 *Merrimac* went into action against a squadron of Union frigates blockading the coast of Virginia. It is said that in a few hours this vessel changed the whole concept of naval warfare; as she approached the Federal warships she came under heavy fire from shore batteries and the opposing frigates but was virtually unaffected. *Merrimac* steered straight for the *USS Cumberland,* a wooden frigate, and rammed her admidships, the *Cumberland* sinking almost immediately with all hands. She then bombarded the *USS Congress,* set it on fire and accepted the surrender of her entire crew.

Apart from the advantages of iron or armour plate it was also noted that the *Merrimac* and the *USS Monitor,* a similar vessel, had been screw propelled and despite intense bombardments (on one day the two of them duelled at point blank range inconclusively for six hours) the propellers had suffered no damage. Like the iron ship the screw took a long time to overthrow the paddle, although in naval circles it was very clearly realised that paddles were vulnerable in action whatever was done to protect them. Yet in spite of Brunel's *Great Britain* there was no general change over the screw propulsion for another 20 or so years. Cunard in particular continued with paddle-wheels until the early 1860s.

In some respects the situation was further confused by the number of pioneers of screw propulsion, all of whom had somewhat different designs. One suspects that the Patent Office was not as careful as it is today and patents were sometimes issued without the proper search. At least 30 different patents were taken out in Great Britain alone before 1850 and a great deal of litigation inevitably followed. About the middle of the century the Admiralty spent a great deal of time and money, not only evaluating the various designs of screw propulsion available, but also in considering the relative merits of screw and paddle propulsion. In 1845 a famous trial took place between the *Rattler*, a screw ship and *HMS Alecto* a paddle frigate of comparable size, hull shape and nominal engine power. Both vessels were tied stern to stern and with the *Rattler's* engine stopped the *Alecto* went full speed ahead. When *Rattler* was ordered 'full ahead' the *Alecto* was not only brought to a standstill but finally towed astern at a speed of nearly three knots. This was the beginning of the end of the paddle-driven vessels in the Royal Navy.

Not that it was all plain steaming for the early screw propellers. Most of the early marine propellers were made from iron, either cast solid in one piece or fabricated in sections and riveted together, and those fitted on vessels sheathed with copper suffered from electrolytic corrosion, which could be severe in vessels that were laid up in harbour for long periods.

More important, the propeller shafts also deteriorated even if they were sleeved with a copper bush. Leakage of water through the stern gland was another source of constant trouble, especially if the stern tube was made of brass which often wore away at an alarming rate—as much as 5lb per day so that water flowed through the stern tube. It was not until John Penn invented the *lignum vitae* bearing in 1855 that this problem was overcome. His bearing comprised an outer gunmetal bush with an internal diameter slightly larger than the shaft journal. The interior of the bush was machined to give a series of grooves into which were fitted *lignum vitae* blocks. providing the bearing surface.

Gearwheels were also subject to rapid wear when they were used to step up the speed of the propeller shaft from the slow-running single-expansion engines.

Even in the 50s coaling stations were few and far between and the engines still demanded enormous quantities of coal; thus it had to be possible to lift the screw out of the water when the ship was proceeding under sail. In some warships the funnel was pivoted at the base so that it could be lowered when the screw was raised and the order. 'up funnel. down screw' became well known in the Royal Navy.

Another invention which occurred in the 1830s but was not accepted for a long time afterwards was Samuel Hall's marine surface condenser. It comprised a shell and tube condenser with an air pipe to draw a vacuum and remove the condensate, a circulating water pump to circulate sea water through the tubes and an evaporator for maintaining a supply of fresh water. This was a considerable advance over the jet condenser invented by Watt and meant that the boilers could steam on fresh water so that the encrustation of brine, necessitating the periodic blowing through of boilers, could be eliminated. The other big advantage was that it could save as much as a third on fuel consumption with a jet condenser.

Hall's condenser was first fitted in the paddle steamer *Prince Llewellyn*, then operating a service between the Menai Straits and Liverpool and also in *Sirius* and *British Queen*. But after a few years shipbuilders began to use jet condensers again because of the extra expense involved. Surface condensers were also liable to become clogged with candle grease which at that time was used to lubricate the moving parts of the engines in preference to oil. It was not until the mid-50s that Hall's invention was re-introduced and by 1860 improved manufacturing techniques made the cost less prohibitive while engineers had been educated to understand the disadvantages of molten tallow.

After the *Great Western* was sold Brunel had occupied himself with a number of tunnelling problems but in 1852 he returned to his interest in ships and prepared preliminary sketches of a vessel which he termed simply 'the great ship'. Because of the great increase in trade which had occurred between Britain and Australia he proposed building a vessel large enough to sail to Australia and back without coaling. His calculations showed that the bunker capacity of such a ship would have to be in excess of 10,000 tons. He put his proposals to the Eastern Steam Navigation Company, which decided to go ahead with the project. However the company stipulated that the ship must call at Calcutta on the homeward journey and this imposed a limitation on the ship's draught because to call at Calcutta it would have to enter the Hooghli River. To overcome this Brunel decided to fit his ship with both screw and paddle-wheels. Normally these would act together but when operating in shallow reaches the paddles only would be used to prevent a serious loss of power if part of the propeller blades projected out of the water.

The first plates of the great ship—it was originally called *Leviathan*—were laid on 1 May 1854 at a yard on the Thames. The paddle engines required were so large that a new shop had to be specially built and the work was undertaken by John Scott Russell, one of the leading naval architects of his day. However, it was Brunel who proposed the cellular construction of the hull, in the form of inner and outer skins which extended from the keel to the water line at a distance of 2.8ft apart. Horizontal iron webs placed 6ft apart divided the space between the two skins into a number of separate compartments. The hull was also divided transversely by iron bulkheads into 10 separate watertight compartments and the longitudinal strength was increased by massive longitudinal frames, two longitudinal bulkheads 350ft long, and a main deck which was also cellular in construction.

The engines were to be the most powerful built up to that time and comprised four horizontal direct-acting cylinders, 84in diameter by 48in stroke to give a total indicated horsepower of 4890 at 38.8 revs per minute. Steam was provided at 25lb per sq in by six double-ended tubular boilers with a total heating surface of 30,000 sq ft. These were the engines for the screw only; the paddle engines were slightly less powerful but consisted of four oscillating cylinders, 74in diameter by 14ft stroke with a total indicated horsepower of 3410 at 10¾ revs per minute. They were supplied with steam from four separate boilers at a pressure of 24lb per sq in and their total heating surface was 19,200 sq ft. The

The *Great Eastern*, docked in 1858

crankshaft for the paddle engines was the largest forging ever made in Britain.

The launching on 3 November 1857 did not augur well. Although it almost became a public holiday, attended by thousands of Londoners who flocked to Millwall, there was both drama and tragedy. One man was killed and four were injured when a cable broke, but the ship, six times the tonnage of any yet built, did not move.

The vessel's great length made a sideways launching imperative and the major problem was to move the hull, which at that stage weighed about 12,000 tons, resting on two cradles, down an incline of 1 in 14 for a distance of 200ft into the water. Further attempts were made without success on 19 and 28 November and then Brunel decided to use batteries of hydraulic presses to move the vessel forward a small distance at a time. In spite of these attempts it was 31 January 1858 before the great ship took to the water. The launching operation had taken all of three months and its cost was afterwards estimated at £120,000.

A new company had to be formed to complete the fitting out of the vessel and about this time the name

The *Great Eastern*
(1858); model

was changed to *Great Eastern*. Brunel, worn out by overwork, went abroad to convalesce and it was not until September 1859 that *Great Eastern* was ready for trials. Just as the ship was due to steam down the Thames to Sheerness Brunel collapsed with a stroke and had to be taken ashore. More disasters followed. One of the feed heaters located at the base of the funnel exploded and three firemen were killed. Brunel himself died a few days later, on 15 September.

Great Eastern went on the Atlantic run in June 1860

Cross-section of
the *Great Eastern*

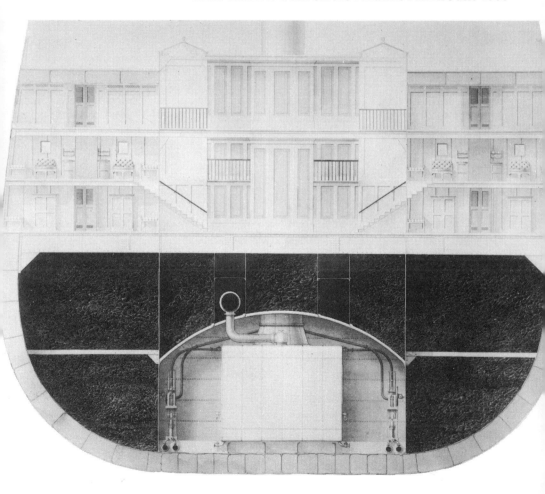

and her maiden voyage was accomplished in 11 days at an average speed of 14 knots. She made several more trips but always seemed dogged by accidents and delays. In a severe Atlantic gale in 1861 her paddle-wheels were destroyed and in the following year she struck a submerged reef at the entrance to Long Island Sound — an accident which might have been disastrous if it had not been for her double hull. As it was, a hole 85ft long was torn in the outer hull although the inner hull remained perfectly sound. The cost of repairs and loss of income because of these two accidents were too much for her owner's precarious financial position and the *Great Eastern* was withdrawn from Atlantic service.

In 1865 she was converted to lay submarine cables and for eight years, until 1873, she laid cables from Europe to America and Bombay to Aden, her great size and excellent manoeuvrability making her ideal for this work. Afterwards she was refitted for passenger service but without success and eventually ended her days as a showboat on the Mersey, until she was broken up in 1888.

Perhaps rather unfairly she was described as 'the greatest failure in the whole history of marine engineering; a premature leviathan conceived and built 40 years in advance of practical experience'. Apart from bad fortune, which dogged her without reason, her major defect was her enormous fuel consumption, the normal rate on the Atlantic run being 330 tons a day — nearly double that of the average contemporary paddle steamer. This disparity could have been justified if she had carried a full complement of passengers but in 1860 there was not the demand for a ship that could carry 4,000 people. In that sense she was some 40 years ahead of her time. However, as the naval historian, K T Rowland, points out, with compound engines she might well have been a great success.

4
THE GREAT
LEAP FORWARD

~~~~~~

In the years 1840 — 1860 a great deal had been done to develop both the iron ship and the principle of screw propulsion. Now it was necessary, urgently necessary, to develop a really efficient steam engine.

Most of the early inventors were practical men with little or no understanding of the laws of physics and at this stage it was a lack of theoretical knowledge which prevented the next step forward. In the years preceding 1860 a belief was still held that the manifestations of heat were due to the action of an imponderable fluid called 'caloric' which had the power of penetrating, expanding and dissolving bodies or dissipating them in vapour. As early as 1824 Nicholas Sadi Carnot, a French physicist, had outlined the true nature of heat and put forward ideas for calculating its mechanical equivalent but his work was ignored and it was nearly 30 years before William Thomson, later Lord Kelvin, and William John Rankine, Professor of Mechanical

Engineering at Glasgow University, re-propounded and extended Carnot's theories.

The work of Thomson, Rankine and others had a great effect on steam engine design and at last removed the dead-hand of James Watt. Watt, of course, made it all possible by inventing his 'improved' steam engine but he set his mind against high working pressures so strongly that he inhibited generations of engineers after him.

Allied to this closer understanding of the properties of heat went an examination of the strength of materials which, for the first time, were evaluated on a scientific basis. Thomas Tredgold, Peter Barlow and Eaton Hodgkinson, for example, made investigations into the properties and strengths of wood, cast iron and other metals and engineers were enabled to work out designs based on accepted material data, rather than just hoping for the best and waiting for the boiler to explode or the piece of machinery to disintegrate.

New materials were also developed. Copper and brass were used extensively in the early steamships because of their resistance to corrosion but had little tensile strength For the first time the technology of using one metal to line another was developed and phosphor bronze was introduced in the middle of the 19th century.

Yet another factor made the big leap forward possible. Fundamental advances in thermodynamics and an increase in metallurgical knowledge were accompanied by improvements in metal fabricating techniques. The adoption of the Whitworth universal screw thread, the development of machines capable of close tolerance work, all encouraged advances.

All these improvements slowly had a cumulative effect in the years 1850 — 1870; the steamship gradually overcame the sailing ship and the screw gradually ousted the paddle-wheel.

What has been described as 'the last and finest paddle-driven vessel' was the *Scotia,* built of iron by Robert Napier & Sons at Glasgow for the Cunard Steamship Co Ltd and launched on 25 June 1861. She renewed the paddle versus screw controversy because she crossed the Atlantic in 1863 from New York to Queenstown in the record time of eight days three hours and held the Blue Riband from 1862 to 1867. She remained on the North Atlantic service for 13 years, the last of the paddle steamers, her eight tubular boilers consuming about 180 tons of coal per day. After being sold in 1879 she was converted into a twin-screw cable ship fitted with inverted two-stage expansion engines. While laying cable in 1896 she suffered a severe explosion on board which blew out the bow and destroyed the collision bulkhead. The second bulkhead held, however, and saved the vessel from foundering, but in 1904 she was wrecked at Guim in the Ladrone Islands.

The *Cutty Sark* under sail

If steam, iron and screws were all winning in the 60s for passenger work they still played a secondary role as far as long distance bulk cargo carrying was concerned. Certainly vessels equipped with the old slow-running single-expansion engines were beaten every time by the famous clipper ships, developed specially for transporting cargoes such as tea and wool half-way across the world.

In the United States particularly, shipbuilders had reacted strongly to the challenge of steam and had considerably improved the sailing ship. The need to build ships which could sail round Cape Horn to California led to the legendary 'Yankee Clippers'. The fast sailing ship reached its zenith between 1860 and 1870 and in 1866 16 British and American clippers competed in a tea race to bring the annual crop from Foochow to London, while in 1868 and 1869 the famous *Thermopylae* and *Cutty Sark* were launched.

However, in 1869 the clippers received a severe blow when the Suez Canal was opened, shortening the route to India and the Far East by several thousand miles. Sailing ships could not use the Canal and steamships took over the lucrative Indian trade. By then many of the steamships were being fitted with compound engines and their improved efficiency, combined with the shorter route, cut coal consumption by as much as 40%.

Indeed, it was the compound engine, with its new capacity to work at high pressure, that finally drove the clippers off the seas. The principle had been known for over 60 years but without the knowledge of how to cope effectively with the higher pressures required. Following Rankine's theoretical work another Glaswegian, John Elder, built the first efficient compound engine to power a seagoing ship. As soon as the engine had been tried out and proved to be effective the ship owners welcomed him with open arms because the compound saved between 30% and 40% fuel when

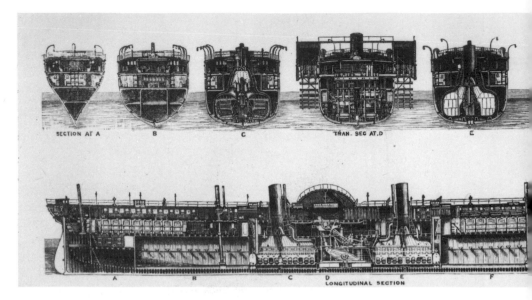

SECTION AT A   B   C   TRAN. SEG AT.D   C

LONGITUDINAL SECTION

A   B   C   D   E   F

Section of *Scotia*

compared with the single-expansion engine of the same power. It was also a more efficient engine in other ways — more regular in movement, thus decreasing the stresses and strains on the rest of the machinery which as a consequence was less prone to break down.

One of the first companies to take up the compound engine was the Pacific Steam Navigation Company, closely followed by the P & O, both of which were engaged in long haulage traffic. The P & O's first ship fitted with a compound engine was *Mooltan,* built in 1861. Five years later the company had 10 vessels in service with this type of engine. About this time the first superheaters were introduced which again increased the thermal efficiency of the coal consumption.

The Admiralty showed an early interest in the compound engine, committed as they now were in greater and greater degree to the steamship. Anything which would reduce the number of coaling stations throughout the world was of importance. One of their earliest

trials concerned three identical wooden sailing vessels which were converted to steam screw propulsion in 1860, two being equipped with simple-expansion engines and the third, *HMS Constance*, fitted with a compound engine designed by Elder. The trial was held in 1865 in the form of a race between the three vessels from Plymouth to Madeira. In fact it was abandoned because all three ships ran out of coal but the superior thermal efficiency of Elder's engine was amply demonstrated.

In 1875 the Royal Navy put compound engines into a number of vessels, including *HMS Rover, Boedicea* and *Bacchante*, all corvettes, and others soon followed.

Twin screws were coming in, too, although very slowly. The first shipbuilder to construct a large number of twin-screw vessels was J & W Dudgeon of Millwall, who completed about 20 twin-screw craft between 1862 and 1865, including eight fast blockade runners, built for the Confederate States. The twin-screw in its earliest form was found to be very effective for small ships, such as blockade runners, where good manoeuvrability and high speeds were essential but it was not until about 1885 that the twin-screw principle came into general use on the North Atlantic service. Screw propulsion, however, gained its final victory over the paddle-wheel in 1867 when the *City of Paris* captured the Blue Riband from the Cunard's *Scotia* by making the Atlantic crossing from Queenstown to New York in eight days four hours one minute, at an average speed of 13.77 knots.

City of Paris was built in Glasgow and launched in December 1865 for the service of the Liverpool, New York and Philadelphia Steamship Company (later known as the Inman Line). At first *City of Paris* was propelled by horizontal simple expansion direct-acting trunk engines of 500 nominal hp with two cylinders each having a diameter of 82in and a stroke of 3ft

6in, which developed a total of 2,600 indicated hp. Steam at a pressure of 30lb per sq in was supplied by eight rectangular fire-tube boilers heated by 24 furnaces which consumed 105 tons of coal a day but in 1870 the vessel was lengthened to 397ft and in 1881 she was refitted with two-stage expansion engines of 550 nominal hp. In 1879 *City of Paris* was a transport ship during the Zulu War and was stranded on a rock in Simon's Bay. She was refloated, however, and finally lost at sea in March 1885 following a collision.

The *City of Paris* was also one of the first steamships to be built of steel — a technical advance as important as the changeover from wood to iron, the latter being very vulnerable to corrosion and fouling. The reluctance of shipbuilders to use steel was largely one of economics. In 1860 wrought iron sold at £8.9s (£8.45) per ton; at the same time steel cost about £50 per ton. The early production of steel was small, too, when compared with iron and it was made by the tedious crucible method invented by Henry Huntsman in the middle of the 18th century. However, the processes invented by Bessemer, Gilchrist Thomas and Siemens rapidly reduced price and increased output. As a result steel began to replace iron as the preferred material of construction during the second half of the 19th century.

The Admiralty was not slow to realise the advantages of the greater tensile strength of steel when compared with iron, and steel made by the Siemens process was used for *HMS Iris* and *HMS Mercury* when they were laid down in 1876.

William Denny of Dumbarton was the man most responsible for the introduction of steel for the hulls of large merchant ships. In 1879 he built a steel hull for the *Rotomahana* ordered by the Union Steamship Company of New Zealand. The first armoured warship to be built of steel in Britain was the *Almirante Brown*, which was ordered for the Argentine Navy.

Her armour was 9in thick and consisted of a layer of steel and a layer of iron which was considered equivalent to 12in of iron armour and reduced the displacement by about 800 tons when compared with a vessel built completely of iron. The year 1876, incidentally, was a landmark in the history of steam navigation because it was the first year in which the number of steamships built in Britain exceeded those under sail. Undoubtedly steel was another factor influencing the outcome of the contest between steam and sail, although the really decisive factor was the introduction of the compound engine.

Yet another development which influenced the acceptance of the steamship was a further improvement in hull design. As we have seen earlier, shipbuilders had, over the years, moved away slowly from the traditional sailing ship designs used for the early steamships but then design concepts had stagnated for some 20 years. William Froude was the man who created the impetus for a further step forward by proving in a series of experiments that a ship's resistance through the water could be deduced from model tests in a tank. Napier had already used a tank as early as 1818, as we have seen, but his work had been forgotten. Froude documented his experiments so closely that naval architects henceforth had a means of checking the performance of their designs before the keel plates were laid.

Coupled with the great advances of the decade 1870-80 there were a number of interesting 'follies' — the circular warships built in Russia, for example, the cross ferry steamer with an entirely 'stable' passenger saloon (it wasn't) designed by the steel-master Henry Bessemer, and the 'ship-within-a-ship' designed for beach landings where there was no harbour and reminiscent of the landing craft used in the Second World War. However, this early effort, designed by a Frenchman, promptly sank off Calais when on its trials.

This era also saw the first twin-hull ships built for the cross-Channel service. One in fact was operated by the London, Chatham and Dover Railway Company for over 10 years and was much favoured for its steadiness by nervous passengers or those prone to sea sickness. She was only withdrawn because she was unable to compete in speed with newly introduced ships.

This was a time, too, when the first of the specialised ships were built. Train ferries were successful from the start and as long ago as 1849 the *Leviathan* had inaugurated the world's first train ferry service for the North British Railway Company, plying across the Firth of Forth from Granton to Burntisland. Another vessel also operated across the Tay at Dundee and both services ran successfully for many years until they were replaced by the bridges.

The first steamship ice-breaker was introduced by the Russians in 1871 and in 1872 the first steamship designed to carry oil in bulk was built on the Tyne. She was known as *Vaderland* and was owned by the Red Star Line of Philadelphia. In design she was remarkably like a miniature of the super tankers of today.

Another innovation which turned out to be a side issue but which dragged on for some 20 years was the motivation of ships by hydraulic propulsion, which had been pioneered in the 18th century. John Ruthven, a pumping engineer of Edinburgh, revived jet propulsion in a practical form in the mid 1860s and captured the interest of the Admiralty. A hydraulic propulsion unit was fitted to *HMS Waterwitch* in 1866, driven by a single-expansion engine. This engine powered a centrifugal pump which took water through a number of openings in the bottom of the hull and discharged the water at a considerable velocity through pipes laid along the ship's sides below the waterline. As we have seen, the Admiralty in those days was a great believer in practical trials but the jet system proved conclusively less efficient than the screw, although the former was greatly preferred by some naval officers because of the risk of fouling the screw especially when the rigging was shot away in action. Until about 1880 the idea of jet propulsion was frequently mooted, but then died a quiet death.

The main stream of development at this time, however, was towards increased thermal efficiencies and consequently lower fuel consumption. Higher steam pressures and improved efficiencies in steam generation depended on improved boiler design and this occupied the attention of many engineers. The 'Scotch' boiler was introduced in 1862. The traditional box-like form was replaced by cylindrical shells and flues to withstand the higher pressure required. From about 1870 onwards the 'Scotch' boiler became the most popular boiler in the British Merchant Marine. It was both sturdy and reliable and suitable for pressures of up to 80lb per sq in. Used with the compound engine it was ideal for the long-haul cargo steamers which were displacing the last generation of sailing vessels.

However, passenger and naval ships required a higher performance and interest was revived in the water-tube boiler which, developed in the early part of the 19th century, had fallen into disuse because of the number of accidents which had occurred in the early versions. J W Rowan and his son were the pioneers of the water-tube boiler as it now emerged. As long ago as 1858 they had fitted a water-tube boiler to generate steam at 115lb per sq in in the cargo vessel *Thetis* built by Scotts of Greenock. The *Thetis* had a compound engine and achieved a remarkably low coal consumption figure of 1.02lb per hp per hour. Unfortunately numerous defects occurred in the boilers and they were removed. The Rowans were hampered in their development of the water-tube boiler by having to use iron as the material of construction: corrosion of boiler tubes was often rapid and sometimes disastrous. Another source of trouble was the accumulation of scale in the tubes, particularly where the bends were acute. This could restrict circulation and cause local overheating and sometimes tube failure.

In the 70s a form of water-tube boiler which generated steam at the very high pressure of 500lb per sq in was installed in a steam yacht owned by Mr Loftus Perkins, an American who lived in Britain. The Perkins boiler was fitted in three small private vessels including his own yacht *Anthracite*, which steamed across the Atlantic and was among the smallest vessels ever to cross the ocean under steam alone. But the Perkins boiler was not successful, mainly because of the high rate of evaporation, which required a boiler feed pump of greater efficiency than was available at the time.

Many other engineers contributed to the development of the water-tube boiler, including the French engineer Julien Belleville who was finally able to produce a satisfactory horizontal version which was adopted by the French Ministry of Marine. The first steel water-tube boilers went a great way towards overcoming the unreliability of those previously fabricated in iron.

Successive developments of the water-tube boiler were made by companies who were concerned with the construction of fast, specialist boats, such as torpedo boats and destroyers for the Admiralty. Two Thames-side engineers were foremost in this development: John Thornycroft of Chiswick and Alfred Yarrow of Poplar.

Thornycroft started his business in 1862 when he was only 19 years old and soon acquired a reputation for building fast steam launches with speeds up to 20 knots at full power. He achieved these speeds by a close attention to hull and engine construction and concentrating on power/weight ratios to a previously unknown extent. In some craft, for example, bored-

102

out piston rods were fitted and his launch *Sir Arthur Cotton*, built in 1874, attained the speed of 21.4 knots on trial and was acclaimed by the London press as the fastest vessel in the world. His steam yacht *Gitania* was the first example of a closed stokehold system being fitted to a British-built vessel. The ash-pits were completely enclosed and the air for combustion was forced in by fans. Increases of power of up to 30% were claimed with the closed ash-pit system patented by James Howden in 1883 and extensively tested in British battleships of the time.

The early torpedo boats, pioneered by Thornycroft and Yarrow, were unique because for the first time in maritime history a new type of vessel had been specially constructed to launch a new type of weapon. At this period in the history of the development of the steamship there is no doubt that the demands of the navies of the world were responsible for greater efficiencies and it was only afterwards that the passenger lines and the cargo-carrying companies benefited from these advances. There was at that particular time very little research or development in the commercial sphere and most of the owners were careful, quite rightly, to choose techniques which were well tried.

Thus it was 1881 before Cunard introduced a steel liner into their fleet. The *Servia* was built by J & G Thomson at Clydebank for the service between Liverpool and New York. Not only was she the first Cunard liner to be constructed of steel but the first to be provided with electric light. She was 544ft long overall and was built with a cellular double bottom, the hull sub-divided by 12 watertight bulkheads, eight of which extended to the main deck. There were three full decks—lower, main and upper, together with an orlop and promenade deck and about 1,250 passengers could be accommodated. She was propelled by a single screw driven by two-stage expansion engines with steam supplied by seven boilers. On trials the

S.S. Servia (1881)

engines attained a speed of 17.8 knots. The *Servia* continued in service on the North Atlantic routes until 1900 when she was used as a transport during the South African war. After a brief return to her former duties she was withdrawn from service in October 1901 and sold for scrap.

While ships of proven reliability such as *Servia* reaped rich revenues for the steamship lines, engineers like Thornycroft and Yarrow were pioneering developments which would be introduced to merchant ships 20 or 30 years later. Thornycroft's first torpedo boat was built for the Norwegian Navy in 1874 and used a compound engine with surface condenser, resulting in a speed of 14.5 knots. Yarrow, meanwhile, was building for the Argentine Navy—fast craft of between 50ft and 75ft long with very narrow beams of only about 8ft. Thornycroft's first vessel for the British Navy was

104

HMS Lightning, equipped with a two-cylinder compound engine which attained a speed of 18.5 knots.

Torpedo boats were in favour and Thornycroft and Yarrow were soon inundated with orders from the navies of the world. Dissatisfied with the existing fire tube boilers Yarrow designed his own and conducted many experiments to study the laws of circulation. His boiler took 10 years to develop and is known among engineers as 'three-drum'; it has since become a favourite with the Royal Navy and navies all over the world. It is simply designed with straight tubes connecting the upper steam drum to the lower water drum. Cleaning and inspection is relatively easy and the design provides excellent circulation. John Thornycroft also produced a notable design for a water-tube boiler, distinguished for its light weight. An early version of it was fitted in the launch *Peace*, built for the Baptist Missionary Society for service in Africa on the Congo River in 1882.

Excited by a new weapon the navies of the world spent years and countless millions in the development of the torpedo boat. It then dawned on them that they might have created a weapon which could do enormous harm to the conventional battleships of the line but which would, itself, be almost invincible by reason of its speed and manoeuvrability. So a new vessel had to be devised which would be fast and powerful enough to hunt down and destroy enemy torpedo boats before they got within firing range. Thus the concept of the destroyer came into being—a concept which was made practical only be the triple-expansion engine which, if successful, could reduce machinery weight still further and offer economies in both space and fuel.

Daniel Adamson must be credited with the first three-stage expansion engine which he built in 1862. John Elder took out a patent for a triple-expansion engine in the same year but apparently did not build it.

In the early 70s Benjamin Normand, a famous French shipbuilder, installed small three-stage expansion engines into a number of vessels. Like other early triple expansion engines they had two cylinders placed tandem-wise and only two cranks.

In Britain Alexander Kirk first demonstrated the triple expansion engine as a viable possibility. Kirk had served his apprenticeship under Robert Napier before going to work as a draughtsman at Maudslay Sons and Field. Later he returned to Scotland and became manager of John Elder & Company at Fairfield, where he supervised the building of *Propontis* in 1873. The vessel itself was only a partial success because the water-tube boilers proved to be unsuccessful but fuel consumption trials convinced Kirk that immense benefits would be gained by expanding the steam in three stages rather than two. The introduction of Siemens steel a few years previously had made it possible to construct boilers that would operate without difficulty or danger at the required pressures and Kirk persuaded the Aberdeen shipping company of G Thomson & Co to fit a triple expansion engine in a vessel for the Australian trade. The *Aberdeen* proved to be a great success and was the prototype of thousands of steamers for the next 50 years. Her engine was an inverted triple expansion with three cylinders and three cranks. Steam was supplied by two double-ended cylindrical boilers at a pressure of 125lb per sq in and the coal consumption on her maiden voyage to Melbourne was only 1¼lb per hp per hour. For the first time the triple-expansion engine made ships of 15,000 tons and more an economic proposition and soon vessels approaching this size were being laid down on Clydebank and Tyneside. The development of the triple expansion engine, incidentally, finally killed off the London-based shipbuilding industry along the banks of the Thames, which was unsuitable for the construction of large vessels.

One of the first passenger liners to be fitted with a triple expansion engine was the *Orinoco* which was built in 1886 for the West Indian mail service of the Royal Mail Steam Packet Company. This was a steel vessel, constructed by Caird & Company of Greenock and was equipped with a triple expansion engine with cylinder diameters of 42in, 62in and 96in. The first liners built specifically for the North Atlantic run and fitted with triple expansion engines were the *Aller*, *Trave* and *Saale* which were constructed by the Fairfield Shipbuilding and Engineering Co Ltd for the Norddeutscher Lloyd Company, the up and coming German line. The sister ship to *City of Paris* already mentioned, *City of New York*, not only had triple expansion engines but twin screws.

A number of Royal Navy cruisers were also among the first ships to be fitted with triple expansion engines although the Italian Navy took the lead with the *Dogali* which had triple expansion engines installed in 1884 to the design of Hawthorn Leslie Ltd. In the following year the British gunboat *Rattlesnake* and battleships *Victoria* and *Sans Pareil* were similarly equipped. The adoption of triple expansion engines soon became general practice for all large ships of the Royal Navy, accompanied by a marked increase in boiler pressures until the high point was reached with *HMS Diadem* in 1898 with 300lb per sq in.

Two of the earliest three-stage expansion sets to be installed in Cunard liners were for *Campania*, launched in 1892 and her sister ship *Lucania*, launched in 1893. Both were built by Fairfield Shipbuilding Company at Glasgow and were intended to regain for the Cunard Steamship Company the leading position in the transatlantic service which about this time they were tending to lose both to other British lines and to Germany. Both liners were very successful and showed advances in size, speed, number of passengers carried and excellence of accommodation. They were each 620ft long overall and built of steel with four complete decks and a promenade deck. In both liners the main engines consisted of two three-stage expansion sets in separate engine rooms placed on either side of the centre line bulkhead. At the steam trials of the *Campania* the engines indicated 31,050hp and an average speed of 23.2 knots.

The *Lucania* was destroyed by fire at Liverpool in 1910; the *Campania* was taken over by the Admiralty in 1914 and converted into a seaplane carrier. She sank in the Firth of Forth in 1918 after a collision with *HMS Revenge*.

The development of the triple-expansion engine gave both Thornycroft and Yarrow the opportunity to supply the answer to the fast torpedo boat. The Admiralty wanted a vessel with a minimum speed of 27 knots, a powerful gun armament and torpedo tubes. In 1893/4 Yarrow's built *Havock* and *Hornet* and Thornycroft's constructed *Daring* and *Decoy*. They were known as 'Torpedo Boat Destroyers' but this was soon shortened to 'destroyer'. In addition to triple-expansion engines both Thornycroft and Yarrow used water-tube boilers. These were so successful that orders for destroyers came in from all over the world and maximum speeds increased with every design. In 1895 *HMS Boxer*, in the second generation of destroyers to be built by Thornycroft's, held the world record with a speed of 29.31 knots. In the following year she was beaten by *Sokol*, a Yarrow-built Russian destroyer which became the first vessel to achieve 30 knots. The battle was on between Thornycroft's and Yarrow and eventually Thornycroft achieved the fastest speed ever reached by a destroyer equipped with reciprocating engines — 31.5 knots, held by the *Albatross*.

For years — in fact until the introduction of the diesel — the triple-expansion engine remained as

108

Cunarder:
the *Caledonia*

standard for most vessels in the merchant service but as steam pressures rose above 200lb per sq in engineers decided to expand yet another stage to obtain maximum economy. The first quadruple-expansion marine engine was fitted in the *County of York*, built at Barrow in 1884, but it was not a success. However in 1894 a five cylinder, four-stage expansion engine was designed by the Central Marine Engineering Works at West Hartlepool and was fitted to the cargo vessel *Inchmona*. It was a success and the coal consumption was as low as 1.15lb per hp per hour.

The quadruple-expansion engine as the most powerful engine afloat had only a short life because it was rapidly superseded by the turbine as the best power unit for fast passenger vessels. However, until the early years of the 20th century quadruple-expansion engines of increasing size and power were constructed for all the leading shipping companies operating on the North Atlantic run. The last large British ship driven by reciprocating engines was the *Asturias*, built by Harland & Wolff, and launched in September 1907. The last Cunard vessel to be equipped with reciprocating engines was launched on the Clyde in 1904

109

Turbinia at speed (1884)

— the *Caronia*, whose twin four-stage engines were probably the largest ever built in Britain. On her trials in February of 1905 the *Caronia* attained a speed of 19.62 knots and ran for some years thereafter at a normal service speed of around 18 knots.

Towards the end of the 19th century Germany was rapidly becoming a major maritime and naval power and in the last days of the old century and the first of the new she built a number of gigantic multi-cylinder engines which were installed in her transatlantic passenger lines, *Kaiser Wilhelm der Grosse, Kronprinz Wilhelm, Kaiser Wilhelm II and Kronprinzess Cecilie*. All these vessels held the Blue Riband in turn and their machinery represented the ultimate development in the steam reciprocating engine — the last 'direct descendant of the simple beam engine developed by Watt'.

But this engine was very soon to be eclipsed by the steam turbine. In 1894 the *Turbinia* was constructed by Parsons Marine Steam Turbine Co Ltd of Wallsend-on-Tyne to demonstrate the potentialities of the steam turbine engine, developed by Sir Charles A Parsons. The yacht was at first propelled by a Parsons' turbine with outward radial flow, which drove one propeller shaft. This proved unsatisfactory and in 1896 it was replaced by a three-shaft arrangement. Each shaft carried three screw propellers and each shaft was driven by a direct-coupled Parsons' turbine with parallel flow. Three turbines were connected in series: steam was first led into the high pressure turbine on the starboard side, then into the intermediate pressure turbine on the port side and finally into the central low pressure turbine. Steam was supplied by a double-ended Yarrow water-tube boiler.

In 1897 *Turbinia* appeared at the Spithead Naval Review, held to celebrate the Diamond Jubilee of Queen Victoria, and amazed and delighted the spectators by attaining a speed of 34.5 knots, a new record.

112

Turbinia (1897); model

The principle of the turbine has been understood for centuries and was demonstrated by the Greek mathematician and inventor Hero, who lived 1900 years ago. Both Watt and Trevithick unsuccessfully attempted to construct the practical turbine. While the leading engine manufacturers were chasing their tails on the problem it was left to Sir Charles Algernon Parsons, the sixth son of an Irish aristocrat, who spent most of his early life in the bogs of the West Coast of Ireland, to discover how to absorb the kinetic energy which is produced by the revolutions of the turbine. In fairness, however, it should be said that his father, the third Earl of Rosse, tucked away in Birr Castle, took a keen interest in machinery and indeed built one of the largest telescopes of the day.

After leaving Cambridge and designing a small epicycloidal engine, Parsons obtained a junior partnership in the Gateshead firm of engineers, Clark, Chapman and Company and became involved in turbines as a means of driving the early electrical dynamos. Turbo-generators to Parsons' design were installed in a number of warships and were soon adopted in power stations ashore.

He then set up a company — Parsons Marine Steam Turbine Company — to consider the problem of using the steam turbine for the direct propulsion of ships. A trial model led to the construction of the *Turbinia*. Following the success of the *Turbinia* Parsons was given an Admiralty contract to equip two vessels, *HMS Cobra* and *HMS Viper* with turbines. Both had four shafts with two propellers on each shaft, although an extra propeller was afterwards added to each shaft of the *Cobra*. On their trials speeds of 35 knots were exceeded and on one run over the measured mile the destroyer *Viper* averaged 37.11 knots. The ships were handed over to the Navy and on 3 August 1901 the *Viper* left Portsmouth to take part in exercises. Unfortunately tragedy was awaiting her and the same day she ran into dense fog near the Channel Islands and at 5.25 in the afternoon struck rocks off Alderney. An hour and a quarter later, the engine and boiler rooms completely flooded, she was abandoned and while there was no loss of life the vessel broke in two and was written off as a complete wreck. She was afterwards destroyed by gunfire to prevent the secrets of her turbine machinery being discovered. Less than two months afterwards *Cobra* suffered a similar disaster when she foundered in a storm off the Lincolnshire coast with the loss of 54 lives.

This double catastrophe was a setback for Parsons because it was alleged at the official enquiry that the turbines had been responsible for breaking up the vessels although it subsequently became clear that structural faults in the hull design were the real cause. However he was given a contract to install turbines for the *King Edward* which was built for Captain John Williamson, chairman of Turbine Steamers Ltd. Captain Williamson was one of the first enthusiasts for turbines for passenger and cargo services and *King Edward* justified the faith of her owner right from the beginning of her service on the Clyde. A sister ship with turbines, the *Queen Alexandra,* was built and yet another turbine steamer, *The Queen,* went into service on the Dover — Calais cross-Channel route.

In 1903 the Admiralty came back for more; *HMS Velox* was fitted out and in the same year cruising turbines were fitted to the destroyer *Eden.*

In 1903, when the Midland Railway Company ordered four new ships for their Irish Sea service it was decided that two of the vessels, the *Londonderry* and the *Manxman* should be fitted with turbines. The *Londonderry*, built at Dumbarton by W Denny Bros and launched in 1904, was 330ft long and could carry 1,600 passengers. During the trials over the measured mile a speed of 22.3 knots was achieved. Both ships were used for the fast service between Heysham and Belfast for many years and in 1927 *Londonderry* was sold to a French company and used for service between Dunkirk and Tilbury and later Folkestone and Dunkirk. She was sold for scrap in 1936.

5
THE BIG SHIPS

The period from 1900 to 1939 might be aptly called the golden age of steam. A century of effort on the part of the inventors and the engineers was now coming to fruition following Parsons' development of the practical turbine. As we shall see, there were many further developments ahead but they have been developments of kind rather than principle.

In the naval field the herald of this golden age was the first *Dreadnought* which entered service in 1906. Built at Portsmouth Dockyard in the record time of a year and a day she was the first 'all-big gun' warship, powered by 10 turbines, the answer to the growing might of Germany. She also heralded a momentous decision by the Royal Navy—that in future all new and refitted ships should be turbine powered. This was largely due to the vision of Admiral Sir John Fisher. Not only was the turbine more efficient, lighter and took up far less space than the quadruple-expansion

116

The Dreadnought

engines but it could be accommodated lower down in the ship and was thus less vulnerable to damage by gunfire. Turbines had fewer working parts and were thus more reliable and more responsive to rapid manoeuvring. Finally at high power there was a considerable saving of fuel.

In the commercial field the famous *Mauretania*, built in 1906, has a place in history comparable with the first *Dreadnought*. She was preceded by the *Virginian* and *Victorian*, sister ships belonging to the Allan Line which were equipped with turbines and went into service in 1904. Even as they were launched Lord Inverclyde, Chairman of Cunard, had put work in hand on the legendary *Mauretania* which was holder of the Blue Riband of the Atlantic for more than 20 years.

117

H.M.S. Powerful

The *Mauretania* introduced the great, glamourous age of transatlantic travel, the splendid, luxuriously appointed, speedy, reliable ships that plied across the Atlantic, carrying the rich and famous. To millions on both sides of the Atlantic who would never travel on them, they epitomised a glittering, graceful life which in some magical way lit up the dreary existence of the mill girl in Wigan or the typist in New York City. This was particularly true in the 30s, perhaps because these gaily lit, apparently carefree ships, sailing steadily through the Atlantic nights, presented such a strong contrast with the dreariness of the depression. And this vision was sedulously fostered by the gossip columnists of the time, by the authors of countless novels and novelettes—and, of course, by Hollywood.

The great *Mauretania* set the scene for all that was to follow. Built by Swan, Hunter & Wigham Richardson Ltd at Wallsend-on-Tyne she was 790ft long with a breadth of 88ft. Amidships she had seven decks, 15

118

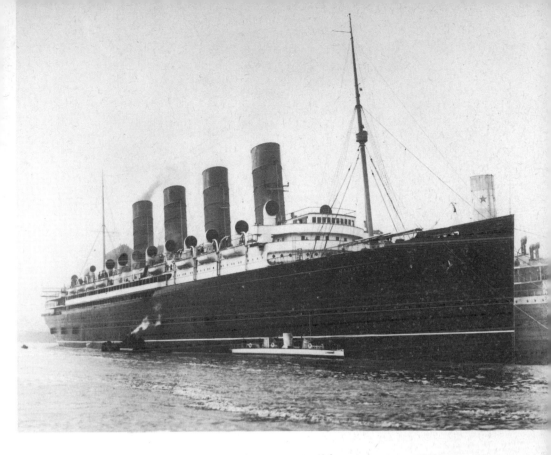

T.S. Mauretania

transverse water-tight bulkheads and a cellular double bottom. Her normal crew consisted of 812 officers and men and accommodation was provided for 560 first class, 475 second class and 1,300 third class passengers. Her quadruple, four-bladed propellers were driven by Parsons turbines of 70,000 shaft hp, giving a speed of 27.4 knots. Steam was supplied by 25 Scotch boilers and more than 6,000 tons of coal could be carried in the bunkers.

During the First World War she served as a troop transporter and a hospital ship and in 1921-22 underwent an extensive refit when the furnaces were converted to burn oil instead of coal. She then resumed the Atlantic service until she was broken up at Rosyth in 1935.

119

For a time Parsons had an almost world-wide monopoly on their turbines but variations were not long in coming. De Laval of Sweden, Rateau of France and Curtis of the United States all took out patents relating to various forms of impulse turbine in which the steam was expanded through a series of fixed nozzles and allowed to impinge upon a row of moving blades attached to the rotor, the action being similar to that of water driving a water-wheel.

Rateau's and Curtis's impulse turbines were particularly successful and the latter's was developed by the General Electric Company of the USA in the first years for driving generating plant. In 1903 the first marine installation was fitted into the steam yacht *Revolution* and this was followed by a much larger contract for the steamship *Creole*, owned by the Southern Pacific Railway. The United States Navy ordered Curtis turbines for the cruiser *Salem* and in 1907, only a year after the launch of the *Dreadnought* in Britain, the comparable battleship USS *North Dakota* was constructed with impulse turbines.

In Britain the Rateau turbine was built under licence by Fraser and Chalmers Engineering Co Ltd of Erith and the Curtis turbine by John Brown & Co Ltd of Clydebank—an association which eventually led to the development of the highly successful Brown-Curtis turbine. This type of turbine offered a number of advantages: blade clearances were not as critical as in the reaction turbine and it was possible to simplify engine room layout. The impulse turbine was more economical at low speeds but lost efficiency to the Parsons reaction turbine as speed increased. The first warship to be fitted with Brown-Curtis turbines was the destroyer *HMS Brisk* in 1909 and this was followed by similar installations in the Acheron Class destroyers of 1911. By the end of the First World War nearly 300 British warships were equipped with this Anglo-American development.

Another early turbine which was widely used in the navies before the First World War was the Zöelly, manufactured by Escher Wyss & Company of Zürich and which consisted of eight high pressure impulse stages with a low pressure portion comprising reaction blading, all within the same casting. The Italian Navy had always had a reputation for speed, one way or another, and one of the Zoelly turbines fitted to the *Animoso* attained 36.12 knots.

Meanwhile Parsons was considering the advantage of hybrid installations which made use of the turbine in conjunction with the reciprocating engine, the idea being to achieve the flexibility of the reciprocating engine with the much greater efficiency of the turbine at low pressures. The *Otaki* built for the New Zealand Shipping Company in 1908 was the first vessel of any size to be fitted with the combined system and it proved very successful. The large White Star liner *Olympic* was also fitted out with the combined system in October 1910 when it was launched at Belfast in the Harland & Wolff yard.

The turbine installations used for *Mauretania* and *Dreadnought* had one inherent disadvantage. They were coupled directly to the propeller shaft and revolved at the same speed as the shaft, so to avoid cavitation their speed was necessarily low. This disadvantage, it was found, could be overcome by fitting a suitable reduction gearing between the turbine and the shaft, leading to greater fuel economy in the order of 15%. In 1911 two cross-channel steamers, *Hantonia* and *Normania* were fitted with geared turbines which gave a top speed of 20.4 knots. In the same year two twin-screw destroyers, *Beaver* and *Badger* were fitted with gearing and the idea was fully developed with the *Leonidas* and *Lucifer*.

The next important development was turbo-electric drive which limited the need for reduction gearing and long shafts, thereby saving weight and making machinery compartments smaller or less congested. The development of the turbo-electric drive was undertaken in the United States and the General Electric Company installed turbo-electric machinery in a number of US naval craft just before the First World War. Following an experiment in the naval collier *Jupiter* which later became the US aircraft carrier *Langley* it was installed in the battleship *New Mexico*.

Geared turbines and turbo-electric drive are the only established methods of propulsion for warships and large passenger vessels today, but in the early days of marine steam engines a third type of reduction gear was developed in Germany which comprised a combination of a centrifugal pump, driven by the main turbine, and a separate water turbine which was coupled to the propeller shaft. Water from the pump passed through fixed guide vanes to enter the secondary or water turbine at the correct angle. Following discharge from the water turbine it was returned to the suction side of the pump so that the action was continuous. Patented by Dr H Föttinger of the Vulcan Werke of Hamburg in 1906 it was used in the liner *Konigin Luise* of the Hamburg-America Line and used on the North Atlantic run. Föttinger's device was also fitted to a number of German destroyers and other ships of the German mercantile marine.

Another innovation, introduced just before the First World War was the use of oil as fuel. The early engineers realised full well that coal is unequally distributed across the face of the earth and the establishment and supplying of coaling stations in ports thousands of miles apart is expensive both to establish and maintain. The first paddle steamers had often used wood which, of course, was incapable of providing enough heat for any but the smallest boilers; tar and creosote were also considered as was oil but in the 1880s the cost of oil in Britain was nearly twice as much as that of coal. Oil-firing first took a hold on the naval and merchant ships of Britain during the early years of the present century but it was not until after the First World War that the North Atlantic steamers such as the *Mauretania* and the *Olympic* were converted. The Royal Navy, however, largely converted to oil-fired vessels during the First World War, although every drop had to be imported through the blockade. Oil-fired vessels have a longer cruising range and can, if necessary, be refuelled at sea. They can also increase speed more rapidly — a very important factor as the submarine warfare intensified. Perhaps the greatest advantage is that smoke can be eliminated if careful control is exercised over the temperature of the oil and the air supply during combustion. The position of a fleet could be kept secret much longer than was the case with coal-burning ships which let out voluminous clouds of black smoke. This great advantage was only demolished during the Second World War when the use of air power and the introduction of radar pinpointed ships even more surely than the black coal smoke.

There was very little general progress in marine engineering during the First World War but one interesting footnote was the use of steam machinery to power two flotillas of Royal Navy fleet submarines. These were the celebrated 'K' submarines produced in response to Admiral Jellicoe's request for support craft for the Grand Fleet. They were equipped with Brown-Curtis turbines for surface propulsion and had a speed of 23 knots.

Now that the steamship was coming into its own across the world it is sad to note that the famous pioneer engine builders were slowly going out of business. James Watt & Company went into liquidation while Maudslay's also closed down in 1901. Humphys, Tennant and Dykes of Millwall provided the machinery for the battle cruiser *Invincible* in 1907 and then closed down; John Penn & Sons lingered on until they had

The ill-fated *Titanic*

completed the battleship *Thunderer* in 1911, when they were absorbed by the Thames Ironworks which itself went out of business just before the outbreak of the First World War. At this time marine engine building on the Thames virtually came to an end. A number of others, who survived the war, went out of business in the post war economic recession. Yarrow's had put all their effort into naval construction and they went into voluntary liquidation at the end of 1921.

After the First World War conversions and refits were the order of the day and in spite of the tremendous losses to merchant shipping there was very little important building. The same applied to the great passenger liners. Shortly before the war the *Titanic* had been lost from the North Atlantic run on her maiden voyage and during the war the *Lusitania*, ill-fated sister of the *Mauretania*, had been sunk, as had many

124

The *Titanic* (1912)

lesser vessels, but it took time for the nations of the world to get on their feet again. Perhaps the only notable exception was a new class of ship, the oil tanker, of growing importance due to the changeover from coal-firing and the rapidly growing popularity of the motor car. The prototype of the modern oil tanker is generally agreed to be the *Gluckauf* which was built as long ago as 1886. After the war the *British General*, built in 1922 was typical of this class of ship. She was built by Palmers Shipbuilding & Iron Company at Jarrow-on-Tyne for the British Tanker Company and was constructed with two decks and 17 water-tight bulkheads. The engines were placed aft and consisted of one high pressure and one low pressure turbine, both connected by double-reduction gearing to the single screw shaft. Steam was supplied by three single-ended boilers fired with oil fuel. She had a normal speed of 11.8 knots and continued in service until October 1940 when she was sunk by a German submarine in the Atlantic.

Just as shipbuilding slowed down for a while so did any developments of consequence in the design of propulsion power. More efficient superheaters were developed and several advance boiler designs were evolved on the Continent, notably Germany, during the inter-war period. Most of these boilers worked on the principle of forced circulation of the feed water and employed an internal pump to boost circulation and increase the rate of evaporation. Among the earliest of this type of boiler was the Benson, invented in 1921, although it was not until 1930 that the first unit was fitted in the *Uckermark* of the Hamburg-America line. In the 30s France, Germany and Italy all experimented with high pressure boilers in ships but most of them gave rise to many difficulties, mainly due to the fact that materials of that time were unsuitable for prolonged service at high temperatures. For this reason 750^0F (400^0C) was the recommended upper limit for British construction until immediately before the second war and the Admiralty frequently preferred to keep well below this figure.

During the inter-war years there was a growing competition to steam by motor ships although they were in the main only smaller craft. The heavy-oil engine was introduced by Dr Rudolf Diesel in 1893 and the first marine diesel engine was built in 1902 for a canal barge. The first motor ship was the oil tanker *Wandel* built at St Petersburg in 1904 for use on the Caspian Sea. The earliest ocean-going motor ship was the Dutch oil tanker *Vulcanus*, built in 1910 at Amsterdam for service in the Dutch East Indies. She had a speed of about eight knots and consumed about two tons of oil per 24 hours. She was successful and remained in service until 1931. The *Carnarvon Castle* was a successful motor-liner. Built in 1926 by Harland

M.S. Vulcanus (1910);
starboard quarter

& Wolff at Belfast she entered the mail service between Britain and South Africa in July 1927 but in addition had excellent accommodation for about 660 passengers as well as seven large cargo holds. She was 656ft long with six decks and 11 transverse water-tight bulkheads. Her normal service speed was about 15 knots with a maximum speed of about 18. In 1938 she was partly re-built and re-engined and her length was increased by 40ft. Her two, by then rather old fashioned, funnels were removed and replaced by a single stream-lined funnel. During the Second World War she served as an armed merchant cruiser and as a troop ship and was finally sold to Japanese ship breakers in 1962.

In the 20s many of the last passenger liners still had

T.S. Arandora Star
(1927)

reciprocating auxiliaries which were replaced by turbo or electrically driven pumps and compressors. The first large British turbo-electric vessel was the *Viceroy of India* which entered service in 1928 for the P & O Company. Following her success P & O laid down two new liners, the *Strathard* and the *Strathnaver* which were similarly equipped.

Other well-known liners of the late 20s and early 30s but which had no particular innovative features were *Arandora Star, Ile de France, Aquitania, Conti de Savoia* and the *Berengaria. Arandora Star* was built by Cammell Laird & Co Ltd at Birkenhead for the Blue Star Line and was launched in 1927. Originally she was intended for the passenger service between London and South America but was converted into a cruising liner — one of the first of her kind. She was

128

constructed with a cellular double bottom and seven decks and the hull was sub-divided by nine transverse water-tight bulkheads. The cabins and public rooms were luxuriously decorated and furnished and she was considered, at the time, to be the epitome of cruise luxury. She had twin screw propellers and these were driven by two sets of Parsons impulse and reaction turbines. Her normal cruising speed was about 15 knots and during the inter-war years she carried thousands of well-off people to the sun and relaxation. However she underwent several major alterations in the 1930s for no very obvious reasons, including the removal of one mast. She was torpedoed and sunk in the Atlantic by a German submarine in July 1940.

Another famous liner of the period was *Empress of Britain*, built by John Brown and Co Ltd at Clydebank for the Canadian Pacific Steamship Company and launched in 1930. She was designed from the start as a dual-purpose ship to be used on the Southampton — Quebec service in the summer and for pleasure cruises in the winter months. She was 760.5ft long and had extremely luxurious and spacious accommodation for about 1,180 passengers. The engines were a four-shaft arrangement of Parsons single reduction gear turbines, each screw shaft driven by an independent set. She had a cruising speed of 24 knots and her steam was supplied by eight Yarrow water-tube boilers and one Johnson boiler. She was disabled by German bombers off the Irish coast on 26 October 1940 and sunk by a German submarine two days later.

Perhaps the most famous of the liners of this period — and an outstanding example of turbo-electric propulsion — was the French *Normandie*. She was the first transatlantic liner to exceed 1,000ft in length and was built by Chantier et Ateliers de Saint-Nazaire and launched in October 1932 for the service between Le Havre, Southampton and New York of the French Line (Compagnie Générale Transatlantique). Her

The liner *Berengaria*

The *Ile de France*

graceful appearance, finely tapered bows, whale-back forecastle, stream-lined funnels and upper work and an absence of ventilators from the promenade decks, made her an instantly recognised sight as she steamed through the Channel — so much so that South Coast holidaymakers in the 30s thought they had been hard-done-by if they failed to catch a glimpse of *Normandie* passing. Her interior appointments lived up to the exterior: she was not only luxurious but furnished in the best traditions of French taste. Even at the height of the depression it was often difficult to get a cabin on her and she was the most popular ship on the North Atlantic run. Accommodation was provided for 930 first class, 680 tourist and 560 third class passengers.

131

Empress of Britain (1930)   *Normandie* had quadruple screws, driven by four independent sets of Zöelly impulse turbines and each turbine was coupled to a three-phase alternator for current at 6,000 volts. Fitted with three bladed propellers she attained a speed on trial of 32.1 knots and in 1937 she gained the Blue Riband, establishing an eastward Atlantic record of three days 22 hours seven minutes with an average speed of 31.2 knots. This ship, perhaps the most graceful steamship ever built, was berthed in New York harbour at the outbreak of the Second World War. She remained at her berth until

December 1941 when, France having fallen the previous year, she was appropriated by the United States Maritime Commission and renamed the *USS Lafayette*. After America came into the war work began to convert her into a troop ship but in February 1942 she was badly damaged by fire and capsized in New York harbour. She was eventually refloated and towed to Port Newark in 1946 where she was broken up.

The *Normandie's* great rival during the 30s was Cunard's *Queen Mary* — the first British 1,000ft vessel and one of the most successful long-serving ships on the North Atlantic crossing. Her machinery followed standard British practice of that period: shafts were each driven by four separate turbines through single reduction gearing. Steam was supplied at 400lb per sq in at a temperature of 700^0F (371^0C) by 24 Yarrow water-tube boilers.

The *Queen Mary* and the *Normandie* fought a continual duel for the Blue Riband. The *Queen Mary* was first successful in 1936 when she crossed the Atlantic in four days 23 hours 57 minutes at an average speed of 30.63 knots. Then in 1937 the *Normandie* recaptured the record after her original propellers had been replaced and in 1938 the *Queen Mary* again won back the Blue Riband for Britain when she completed the crossing at an average speed of 31.7 knots.

From the first it was always the Cunard Company's intention that *Queen Mary* should be complemented with a vessel of similar size to maintain a weekly ser-

Normandie (1932)

Queen Mary (1934)

vice between Southampton and New York and thus her sister ship, afterwards named *Queen Elizabeth*, was laid down at the Clydebank yard of John Brown & Company Ltd in 1936. She was launched on 27 September 1938 but was not completed at the outbreak of war. In March 1940 she sailed secretly to New York and then served as a troop ship, returning to the peacetime Atlantic service in October 1946. When she went into peace-time passenger service she had already steamed about half a million miles. The *Queen Mary* was retired at the same time and is now the principal attraction in a recreational complex at Long Beach, California. She had been radically altered for her new role as a floating hotel, museum and conference centre but much of the original fabric has been retained and

is reported to be in excellent condition. The *Queen Elizabeth*, less happily, became a gaming complex in Florida, and was later destroyed by fire in Hong Kong.

The main machinery of the *Queen Elizabeth* was similar to that of the *Queen Mary* and her four shafts were driven by four sets of Parsons single reduction geared turbines but only 12 Yarrow boilers were required instead of 24 and steam was generated at 450lb per sq in and superheated by 750⁰F (400⁰C), about the upper limit in British pre-war practice.

Queen Elizabeth had a well-raked stem and a full cruiser stern, 14 decks and was 1,031ft in length. Her hull was sub-divided by 15 transverse water-tight bulkheads and the cellular double bottom comprised

Queen Mary under construction (1934)

Queen Elizabeth (1938)

more than 50 main compartments. Accommodation was provided for 822 first class passengers, 668 cabin class and 798 tourist class, with a crew of 1,250 officers and men.

Although few fundamental advances were made in steamship design during the war years, metallurgical and design innovations have ensured that the failures that occurred in many of the pre-war high pressure installations were not repeated and thus there are a great deal more high pressure, high efficiency boilers in service today. New and improved steels such as chrome-nickel-vanadium steel were brought into service for turbine rotors and molybdenum-bearing steels were used for operating temperatures in excess of $850°F$ ($454°C$). Similar progress was achieved with other machinery components, the most important being the introduction of oil-hardened and tempered nickel-chrome-steel pinions for reduction gearing. These had improved tensile strengths compared with the earlier types, which were in nickel steel.

6 THE STEAMSHIP TODAY

During the post-war period a number of notable passenger vessels have been built for both the North Atlantic and the increasingly lucrative Australasian services although the ever-increasing competition of air travel has led to a severe reduction in passenger traffic across the Atlantic by sea and many of the largest companies have found themselves in financial difficulties. Gone forever, it would seem, are the luxury liners of the 30s and today the one-class ship with large elements of self-service, which would horrify the first class passenger of 50 years ago, is the name of the game.

Since the war there have been some changes in the traditional arrangements of locating machinery spaces amidships. The first vessel to locate its machinery compartment aft was the *Southern Cross*, built for the Australasian service by Harland & Wolff in 1954. This arrangement permits far greater freedom in the

138

design of passenger saloons and lounges which are, as a result, entirely free of machinery casings. A similar arrangement of locating the machinery aft was followed in the *Canberra*, which was also built by Harland & Wolff at their Belfast yard. Although she is much larger she resembles the *Southern Cross* in general appearance and has a turbo-electric drive. The *Canberra* was the largest passenger liner built in Britain between the *Queen Elizabeth* completed in 1940 and the *Queen Elizabeth II* (QE2) ordered in 1965. The turbo-electric machinery is by far the most powerful equipment of this type installed in any British vessel although her output is still less than that of the *Normandie* in the 1930s.

In addition to turbo-electric propulsion the construction of the *Canberra* includes a number of features which are today regarded as standard practice. The most notable is the use of aluminium alloy for the fabrication of the entire superstructure, which reduces top weight and also allows for additional accommodation. Aluminium was also extensively used in the Orient Line vessel *Oriana* and the first vessel of any size to feature an all-welded aluminium structure was the British built Norwegian liner *Bergensfjord* constructed in 1955-6.

Although the writing was on the wall for the transatlantic 'big ship' by the mid-50s, the American Government decided to build the *United States*. On 8 February 1950 the keel of the largest passenger ship ever built in the United States was laid down at an estimated cost of 77 million dollars, of which the United States Line, which was to operate the ship on the Atlantic crossing was to contribute 32 million dollars, while the US Government promised to absorb 45 million. It was known from the start that she must fulfil a dual role. She would be a money earner, carrying tourists back and forth from Europe, but in the event of another war she should be capable of adaptation to a

The *Canberra*

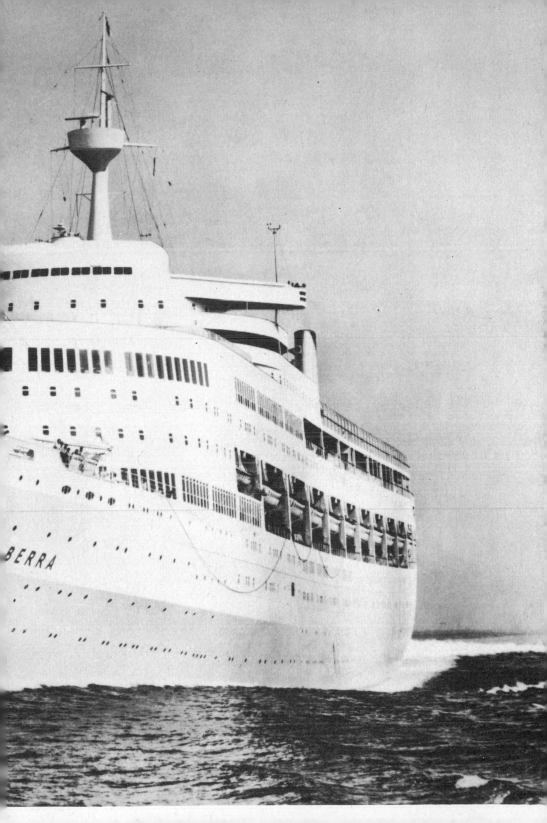

The *United States* (1951)

troop ship. She was floated out—rather than launched—on 23 June 1951, a ceremony attended by President Truman and Mrs Truman, who named the liner. The main propulsion turbine, boilers and auxiliaries were arranged to be operated as four independent units. The double reduction geared turbines were supplied by the Westinghouse Electrical Corporation of Pittsburgh and the boilers by Babcock and Wilcox of New York. Passenger accommodation was for 1,962 passengers—882 first class, 525 cabin and 555 tourist class. This accommodation did not quite match up to the high standards of the *Queen Mary* and *Queen Elizabeth* but it was certainly good enough for the times. Great emphasis was laid on the need for the liner to be virtually fireproof and for this reason light metal and

142

aluminium were used in the furniture and other decorative features. As with the *Canberra* and *Oriana* aluminium largely replaced steel in the liner's superstructure and in such features as the two funnels, single mast and lifeboats. When she put to sea for trials in June 1952 it was obvious that in her exterior appearance she conformed to tradition. She had a slightly raked stem, long sleek hull, single short mast and two large funnels.

On 3 July 1952, under the command of Captain Harry Manning, Commodore of the United States Line's fleet, she set out on her maiden voyage to Le Havre and Southampton carrying, among a full passenger complement, Miss Margaret Truman, daughter of the President. She completed the passage in three days 10 hours and 40 minutes (an average speed of 35.59 knots). On her return journey she made three days 12 hours and 12 minutes at an average speed of 34.51 knots. To these speeds the *Queen Mary* and the *Queen Elizabeth* had no reply and American citizens all over the world were triumphant. For the first time in 100 years an American-built passenger liner had won the Blue Riband. The previous American-built holder had been the Collins' wooden paddle steamer *Arctic* which, in 1852, had deposed the Cunard paddle steamer *Asia* by a voyage from New York to Liverpool in nine days 17 hours 12 minutes at an average speed of 13.25 knots.

For the next 17 years the *United States* maintained sailings across the Atlantic; satisfied with the record of her maiden voyage record she never improved upon it but then neither did any other ship. One by one the giants fell away. On 8 May 1967 Sir Basil Smallpiece, Chairman of Cunard, announced that over the next two years there would be a 'phased withdrawal' of the *Queen Mary* and *Queen Elizabeth* because the ships were no longer economic. One million passengers had crossed the North Atlantic by sea in 1957; by 1965 the

The *QE2*

total had dropped to 650,000. Over the same period, passenger traffic by air had increased from one million to four million a year. Tom Hughes, the maritime historian has said, 'the Atlantic Ferry had taken wings. The day of the Blue Riband ships was ending.'

For a short time longer the *United States* remained in service then on 15 November 1969, the centenary year of the maiden voyage of the pioneer US paddle steamer *Savannah*, it was announced that the United States Line had decided that, for economic reasons, she should be laid up. For nearly four years the last and unchallenged holder of the Blue Riband remained idle until on 10 February 1973 came the news that she

144

had been purchased by the US maritime administration. They paid 4.6 million dollars.

The only post-war vessel which has approached the performance of the *United States* is the French liner *France* and for many years the two vessels operated alternate schedules on the Atlantic service. The *France* was built by Chantier de L'Atlantique de St Nazaire, the shipyard responsible for the *Normandie* and her maiden voyage took place on 3 February 1962. She was the second liner of that name, the first *France* having been launched 50 years earlier. Another large liner built in the post-war period and still in service is the *Rotterdam*, 38,645 tons. The

S.S. United States
and *S.S. America*

Queen Elizabeth II of 58,000 tons built by John Brown & Company and which suffered so many teething problems, was launched in 1967 and was designed at the outset as a dual-purpose ship for the Atlantic service in the summer and for pleasure cruising during the winter months.

Since the war the United States Navy has been active in the development of high pressure boilers but perhaps their greatest contribution to the advancement of marine engineering has been the development of nuclear-powered craft, first submarines and subsequently surface vessels. In these craft the nuclear plant is a pressurised water reactor which supplies steam to drive the turbines, which in turn drive the propeller shafts. The principal advantage of the nuclear plant

The *QE2* (another view)

over conventional oil- or coal-fired boilers is that it can be operated for very much longer periods without refuelling.

Many eminent American engineers and physicists co-operated in the design and construction of the first nuclear-powered submarine—the *USS Nautilus,* working under the direction of Admiral Hyman G Rickover, USN. On 17 January 1955, on the occasion of her first sea trial the historic signal was made 'underway on nuclear power'. The unqualified success of the *Nautilus* encouraged the United States to build an entire nuclear submarine fleet and 31 vessels were laid down during the years 1961-6.

Several nuclear-powered surface vessels soon followed. By far the largest, and indeed the costliest ship ever built at a price of nearly £160 million, is the aircraft carrier *USS Enterprise* which is equipped with eight pressurised-water reactors and 32 heat exchangers. The main propulsion comprises four sets of geared turbines giving a top speed of between 33 and 35 knots and a radius of action without refuelling of an incredible 140,000 miles. At a cruising speed of 20 knots the

Nuclear ship
Savannah (1959)

range is extended to 400,000 miles, which in practice means nearly five years without refuelling. The second of these carriers is *USS Nimitz*, the keel of which was laid on 22 June 1968.

The other nuclear-powered surface ships in the United States Navy are the guided missile cruiser *Longbeach* and the guided missile destroyers *Bainbridge* and *Truxtun*. *Longbeach* can steam for 100,000 miles at its top speed of 30.5 knots and 360,000 miles at a cruising speed of 20 knots. The *Bainbridge*, which was completed in November 1962 can steam at 30 knots for 150,000 miles and 400,000 miles at a cruising speed of 20 knots.

T.S. Zenatia

The earliest non-military nuclear-powered vessel was the Russian icebreaker *Lenin* who made her maiden voyage in 1959. She is equipped with three pressurised-water reactors and main propulsion is by turbo-electric machinery. The steam from the reactor heat exchangers is supplied to three turbo-generators, which in turn provide power for a single motor connected to the centre shaft and two smaller motors for the wing shafts. The reactors are said to operate for a year without refuelling and the *Lenin* can work in 6ft of ice. In three seasons in the Arctic the *Lenin* steamed 57,500 miles and consumed 36 kilograms of uranium; in a conventional ship the same distance would have required about 18,000 tons of coal or 10,000 tons of fuel oil.

The first atomic merchant ship was the *Savannah*, built in the USA and launched in 1959. The *Otto Hahn* was launched in Germany in 1964 as a cargo-passenger ship and has an advanced pressurised-water reactor to provide power to drive a single shaft, giving a cruising speed of 15¾ knots. The *Mutsu*, launched in Japan in 1969, is another atomic-powered merchant ship.

It is very difficult to find out much about the operating costs of these vessels although it is known that the *Savannah* had been heavily subsidised during her period of commercial service with the American-Isbrandsen Line and has now been withdrawn for economic reasons. It must be very difficult indeed to obtain any large return on initial capital investment which could easily run as high as £50 million. Not only is a large capital investment required but fuel costs are at least two or three times as high as those of conventional vessels powered by oil-fired steam turbines or diesel engines.

Another post-war development that must be mentioned but which has not entailed any new principles of propulsion are the supertankers and the super-

supertankers. In the mid-50s oil tankers like the *Zenatia* in the Shell fleet created mild sensations because of their size which might be as much as 38,000 tons dead weight. Shell at this time added a large number of new vessels to her fleet, some of which were built by Cammell Laird & Co Ltd at Birkenhead and — a sign of the times — in 1966 a number of them were enlarged. The *Zenatia* was one which was originally 675ft long and became 842ft long, with her dead weight increased to 69,956 tons. By 1970 these sorts of figures were chick-enfeed and tankers with a length of 1,132ft and of 312,000 tons dead weight were rapidly becoming commonplace. At this moment of writing many of them are laid up and controversy rages about the economic viability of such large tankers; indeed there is a swing towards middle-sized vessels of 100,000 tons or less. Another development with great potential is that of Container ships.

While nuclear propulsion has overshadowed any other marine engineering developments during the last 15 years there have been a number of unspectacular but nonetheless important advances. For example, a great deal of effort has been devoted to improving the efficiency of the screw propeller. New materials have replaced manganese bronze which has been used for large vessels for nearly 60 years. Copper-based alloys such as nickel-aluminium-bronze and copper-manganese-aluminium alloys are less susceptible to cavitation erosion. Stainless steel is also being employed for propeller castings.

The propeller of counter-rotating design was first conceived by John Ericsson in 1837 and during the last few years has aroused interest again. Counter-rotating propellers are fitted to the American nuclear submarine *USS Jack* and are said to produce a 10% increase in power efficiency.

Many experiments — as yet inconclusive — have been carried out to ascertain if efficiencies can be

152

United States Lines,
S.S. American Astronaut
(another view)

improved by increasing the number of blades to a propeller and the Japanese have tested prototypes with
seven blades. An entirely new propeller, the Voith-
Schneider propeller has also been tried. It is in fact a
combined propeller and rudder and it gives extreme
manoeuvrability. The possibility of dispensing with
propellers altogether is still being actively pursued and
a number of patents have been granted during the last
10 years for various forms of jet propulsion.

The golden days of the great luxury passenger liners
are almost certainly ended — although there will

always be some people who prefer to go in comfort and at leisure across the world rather than sustain the boredom and fatigue of trans-world jet travel. But it is difficult to believe that the steamship as a cargo carrier, or cruise ship, will become obsolete. The steamship's really great days of invention, innovation and adventure are over but it is still a vital part of our international communications system, and will long be remembered as the ultimate symbol of more leisured days, long gone.

INDEX

156